G000097411

AN
INTRODUCTION TO
MODERN NURSERY STOCK PRODUCTION

AN INTRODUCTION TO **MODERN NURSERY STOCK PRODUCTION**

LILA DICK

FREDERICK MULLER LIMITED, LONDON

First published in Great Britain 1982 by
Frederick Muller Ltd., Dataday House, Alexandra Road,
Wimbledon, London SW19 7JZ

British Library Cataloguing in Publication Data

Dick, Lila
Modern nursery stock production.
1. Plant propagation
I. Title
631.5'37 SB119

ISBN 0-584-10410–3

Photoset by Input Typesetting Ltd, London
Printed in Great Britain by The Anchor Press Ltd.,
Colchester, Essex.

To Dolly, Ian, John and Tommy who have patiently and tolerantly put up with my 'ideas' in the nursery.

Acknowledgments

My thanks to Ian Baldwin, B. & S. Business Studies, Ridgeway, Limecroft Road, Knaphill, Woking, Surrey, GU21 12TH, for the chapter on Nursery Economics. To the Principal and the Head of Department of Horticulture and Bee-Keeping at the West of Scotland Agricultural College. To Ian G. Walls – for his editing, help and encouragement. To C. W. Taylor for his photographic skills, to Javo b.v. Holland and Dorrell Bros. and Blooms Nurseries Ital., for allowing their photographs to be reproduced. To A. MacQueen for his artistic drawings and Mrs C. Telfer and Mrs K. Blair for their heroic efforts in coming up with the typed end-product! To anyone whose work is referred to in the text and is not mentioned personally.

Contents

Introduction

The transportation of plants and the cultivation of nursery stock is a very old practice. In the earliest centuries before Christ the Egyptians brought plants from the Sudan to grow in their own lands by the Nile while the Romans, when they had conquered Britain, imported many trees and shrubs into their new province: the sweet chestnut, the walnut, the common lime and the mulberry. They greatly enriched our plant legacy for only 2% of the trees and shrubs in Great Britain are 'native' species, that is plants indigenous to this country. One of our most common native trees is the Scots pine and, according to W. J. Bean's *Trees and Shrubs Hardy in the British Isles*, the common elm which sadly today has been virtually extinguished by the Dutch elm disease which has ravaged our countryside.

Many plants were originally cultivated for medicinal purposes, and in the middle ages many rare plants were collected and grown by monks in the monastery kitchen garden both for medicinal purposes and to supply the monastery with food. Many monastic gardens are still being cultivated today while some of those trees planted by the monks in the middle ages are still standing long after the monasteries have fallen into ruin: two lovely sweet chestnuts still grow near the kitchens of the ruined Priory of Inchmahome on the lake of Menteith, Scotland.

One of the earliest professional nursery stock producers was John Tradescant the Younger who brought back from his travels in North America *Robinia pseudoacacia* (locust tree), *Juglans cinerea* (walnut called butter nut) and *Acer rubrum* (red maple) which he cultivated in his nursery and had listed in his 1656 catalogue. By this time plant hunting expeditions were part of the horticultural scene and the adventures of these brave men would make a James Bond film look like a nursery rhyme. Cloak and dagger intrigues, being hunted by wild natives, falling into animal pits, losing the way, breaking legs and succumbing to dangerous epidemics were all part and parcel of their journeys.

Despite the dangers, plant collecting continued at a steady pace with more and more countries being explored for their native plants. As plant hunting increased botanic gardens were established by many of the great universities: Oxford in 1621, Edinburgh in 1670. Here imported trees and shrubs could be propagated and soon land owners began to utilize newly propagated specimens to re-forest their estates. The 2nd Duke of Atholl, known as 'the Planter', took such a liking to the larch which had been introduced in 1620 that he planted enormous numbers of them.

In the London area many nurseries were doing business at this time in what was then pleasant countryside on the outskirts of the city. James Gordon had established a nursery at Mile End, James Lee at Hammersmith and Conrad Loddiges at Hackney. In 1725 T. Rivers moved further afield and opened his nursery in Hertfordshire. All these nurseries were supplied with new stock gathered by the great travellers and plant collectors such as David Douglas who journeyed through North America and brought back the great fir *Abies grandis* commonly known as the Douglas fir. He also introduced several new shrubs such as *Garrya elliptica, Ribes sanguineum* and *Galtheria shallon.*

E. H. Wilson was probably one of the greatest plant collectors of all time and an indefatigable purveyor of nursery stock. From his travels in China, Japan, Australia, New Zealand, Singapore, India, Sri Lanka and South and East Africa he brought back over 1,200 specimens of trees and shrubs, among them the lovely Kurume azaleas.

Today many expeditions to collect new plants are sponsored by Botanic Gardens and various horticultural societies. H. F. Comber has introduced from the Chilean Andes four new types of *berberis* and *Fabiana imbricata*, E. D. Merrill has worked closely with Chinese collectors and in 1948 introduced the Dawn Redwood (*Metasequoia glyptostroboides*), while more recently Roy Lancaster formerly of Hillier's Arboretum has been on several expeditions.

China too is opening her doors to plant hunters once more. After many years of exclusion this country, with many areas rich in plant life, will be a good hunting ground.

The 20th century has given us new cultivars of plants as well as a keen awareness of selection, be it for hardier specimens (always a problem for American nurserymen in the colder zones), or disease resistance, colour sporting and special characteristics such as leaf shape or growth pattern. Clonal selection is now being investigated in this country (it is already standard practice in many countries).

Plant selection is an age old practice but today there is a danger that commercial selection, which all too often is a selection and perpetuation of those plants which are easy to grow, will lose for us many good plants, and it is to be hoped that Botanic Gardens and the Royal Horticultural Society gardens will continue to preserve collections of plants likely to be lost through large scale cultivation.

Chapter 1

Production trends

Nursery stock producers are obsessed not only with what is presently in demand, but also with what possibly *will* be in demand in the future. One must be aware not only of trends but also of major events. The Queen's Silver Jubilee in 1977 is a good example, when trees were in huge demand. Alternatively one can grow plants and then advertise them lavishly as was the case with *Potentilla* 'Red Ace'.

Other 'indicators' are the creation of motorways, massive new buildings, home ownership, complexes or developments, national parks, plants for low maintenance or to replace the ravages of Dutch Elm disease. All these give some idea of the type of plants likely to be needed for particular purposes, and the object is to be ready to supply the anticipated demand. Roses have been an integral part of British gardens for centuries and it is only in recent years that they are declining in popularity. Rose growers, however, are quick to bring out new cultivars for specific purposes, e.g. the Queen's Silver Jubilee. Councils and firms sponsor new roses to keep them in the public eye. The rose industry plays an important part in British horticulture, and this includes the increase of home-grown rose root stocks to reduce imports. With the majority of householders working full-time most have little time to spend in their gardens unless it is their main hobby. So a garden which is easy to maintain is the aim and this includes patio areas, plantings of shrubs, ground cover and heaths and heathers. These outlets all have to be supplied with plants, creating an increasing demand for nursery stock. As leisure time increases and the cost of running a car becomes higher, surely the 'back yard' or garden could become a more important facet of life, for sitting in or for growing food? The interest in garden programmes on TV and radio shows the thirst that exists for knowledge on all gardening subjects.

Market Surveys

The production trends referred to earlier may give pointers to nursery stock producers, as can actual sales figures and stocks of plants left at the end of the gardening season. Plants asked for but not available 'in the trade' should also be carefully noted. A typical example is the way the demand for *X Cupressocyparis leylandii* as a hedging plant has been maintained over many years. There is the situation too where a plant in demand two years ago is produced in quantity, loses favour or is over-produced and a glut arises. Reading the trade papers or conducting your local surveys is also a good approach to likely demands. Producing plants which will grow well in a specific area pays dividends. If a reputation for quality and reliability can be built up people will come to you. Heathers plus bags of peat in a tourist area can be a money-maker but if petrol is in short supply this can keep customers away. A stall at the local market or flower show may be the answer for finding out what is in demand. Giving a talk to flower clubs and women's Rural Institute Meetings is a good public relations exercise and at the same time ascertains local needs.

Organized market surveys are nevertheless still important as the nursery-man has to be guided on which plants to grow. Consumer surveys, noting what bargains or discounts are being offered to new householders, finding out what plants sell faster in Supermarkets and garden centres can give some indication, but most garden centre proprietors will say if a plant is in flower there is a good chance of selling it! 'Plant of the month' schemes help, providing you have an adequate supply of the plant and seasonal demand for such plants as natural Christmas trees rather than artificial ones must be taken into account. All this can give the nursery stock producer ideas but unfortunately there are no hard and fast rules to follow.

Types of units and outlet

Wholesale

This type of nursery grows exclusively for the trade, and in many cases will supply garden centres. Large quantities of plants are grown and sold by the thousand. They are as fully mechanized as possible, and will have large irrigation systems. More often than not they have specially adapted transport and a good delivery service.

Catalogues for this type of enterprise are not usually sophisticated as what is needed is the list of plants and the wholesale prices. The customer will know his plants and only wants basic information. One or two wholesale growers do have coloured pictures (usually a co-operative with a combined catalogue, thus sharing the high cost of production).

Wholesale/Retail

This can consist of a wholesale business which also has retail outlets: shops, smaller nurseries, or more recently garden centres. Usually such a grower will also supply other outlets as well as his own. It may well be a company and often smaller businesses are bought, keeping the original name for trading purposes.

Retail

This applies nowadays to a wide variety of outlets, where plants are simply bought in and re-sold. It may be a nursery or garden centre which grew plants, but found the economics of growing and retail did not combine satisfactorily and retail has taken over. Many other places have proved to be areas for selling, such as supermarkets, petrol stations, ironmonger shops, chain stores, stalls in the markets, auctions, shows of all kinds. Indeed it is remarkable where nursery stock can be sold.

Mail Order

As an outlet for plants mail order relies on catalogues, newspapers, especially the Sunday papers and all types of magazines which display a profusion of fantastic looking or unique plants offered because the seller is relying on this method to reach his customer. Tips and instructions are given, there are additional tempting offers to include tools or other items and large store mail order catalogues invariably have a section on horticulture these days. Mail order is considered to be the traditional method of selling plants and fits in well with open ground production as opposed to pot or container grown items. It is especially suited for roses, small plants, bulbs and seed. The upsurge of garden centres has to some extent seen a decline in the mail order business but the high cost of motoring seems to be acting as a boost to it again. However, since the postal service will only take parcels up to 25 lbs. (11.3 kg.) and the cost of road and rail services for heavy items has increased, it probably means it is just as cheap for the man in the street to go to the nearest garden centre and select his plants on the spot.

Garden Centres

These have presented the most revolutionary aspect of horticultural trade in the past decade. It has brought the public in direct contact with plants, but to be really successful garden centres must have large car park areas, toilet facilities, coffee shops, sundry items, garden furniture, weed-killers, pesticides, etc. A whole range of garden and associated products must be offered if they are to do well and help to even out the cash flow ups and downs inevitable with a trade which is so affected by seasons and the weather.

Chapter 2

Areas of commercial importance for nursery stock producers in Britain and abroad

Originally nursery stock producers were centred near London but as the town expanded land was developed for building purposes. Surrey then became the main area of production and the greatest number of nurseries in the U.K. are still to be found there.

Nearness to customers is no longer so necessary as the rail and road systems have developed and transportation of plants has speeded up. Nurseries can be sited today in areas which at one time were thought to be inaccessible and a grower need no longer rely on good soil as all his plants can be grown in containers on a concrete base or a disused airport runway if he feels inclined!

Other considerations have an important bearing, such as whether the climate is favourable, if financial aid is given in the form of Government grants to the nursery stock industry as it is in Eire, or by the Highland and Islands Development Board in areas of Scotland. More co-operatives have been formed with Government financial help such as the Anglia Group, Midland, Northern Nurseries and the Border Shrub Group. Figure 1 is intended as a rough guide of the location of the industry in the U.K. but by no means includes every nursery.

Holland

The oldest production area is situated at Boskoop, having approximately 1,000 nurseries on 1,500 acres (607 hectares). Exports amount to 90% of all stock grown and this is transported to Canada as well as European countries. A plant protection service controls the health standards of the crops grown for export. Boskoop has an experimental station which caters for the needs of the nursery stock industry and studies work efficiency methods as well as plant problems.

The soil in this part of Holland is ideally suited for open ground

Figure 1 The distribution of nurseries in Great Britain, Eire and the Channel Islands.

production of nursery stock, being very peaty which allows plants to root-ball easily. This could be the reason why container growing has not developed so fast as it has in other countries. The high water table of Boskoop area due to the canal system also has a bearing on production. Nevertheless, many growers are moving out of the Boskoop areas and setting up nurseries in other parts, as land prices are prohibitive. Canals too are being filled in to make it easier to transport plants from the nurseries. There is a large rose root-stock co-operative at Groningen in an area of the country which has 500 hectares of rose root-stocks. At Brabant and Limburg there is the largest amount of nursery stock to be found in Holland. Plant Propaganda Holland (P.P.H.), situated at Boskoop, covers publicity and produces fine coloured posters for all types of nursery stock. This is one reason why Holland's nursery stock industry is so successful.

Germany

The largest number of nursery stock producers of roses, deciduous trees and shrubs, and conifers are to be found in the Schleswig-Holstein area. The headquarters of the B.d.B. (Bund deutscher Baumschulen), a co-operative group, is at Pinneburg. Voluntary pest and disease control is carried out giving the B.d.B. seal of approval which helps both grower and purchaser. The other important area is Niedersachsen where 61% of German evergreen trees and shrubs are produced.

Denmark

Here a highly efficient plant production service is controlled by the Government and there are over 900 nurseries of which 120 account for 95% of plant production, many of them using cold stores for nursery stock production to allow a longer dormant season. The Danish nurserymen have their own co-operative association and advisory staff and also an experimental station situated at Hornum. Co-operative groups are very successful, with experienced staff employed by the co-operative for sales and publicity, and often use a trade name such as Danplanex.

France

Areas of production in France are situated in the Loire Valley both at Orleans and Angers. Although stock is produced along traditional lines, new ideas are also being developed. The Government is encouraging nursery men to expand outside Orleans and land has been set aside for this purpose. Again co-operation and an efficient use of resources is evident. 'Plandorex' is a co-operative group of nurserymen and another co-operative 'Gexplant' exports to the U.K.

Belgium

Certain facets of the Belgian horticultural industry concentrate on nursery stock which is handled largely through co-operatives – with superb publicity.

Other countries with important nursery stock production are the U.S.A., Australia, New Zealand and Israel, with countries such as Kenya, Pakistan and even Saudi Arabia beginning to produce plants.

The message is quite clear, however, that if a nursery stock is to develop satisfactorily – it must be highly organized – with good technical back-up and publicity.

Chapter 3

Stock plants

In any production programme the importance of stock plants cannot be over-stressed. Stock plants are a crop in their own right and should be treated as such with regular pruning, feeding and weed control for it is from these plants that the nurseryman will obtain his future plants either as cuttings or as a seed source.

The range of stock plants is very wide, far wider than for other sectors of horticulture, and includes the production of rose **root-stocks**, **roses** themselves, **fruit tree root-stocks**, budded or grafted **fruit trees** (both edible and ornamental), **trees** of all shapes and sizes, **shrubs** both half hardy (limited in their use) and hardy. (After the severe winter of 81/82 we may have to re-consider what is truly hardy!) **Heaths and heathers**, **climbing plants** such as clematis which can be a specialist line, **herbaceous plants**, **ground cover** (a term applied more to the habit of plant growth than to any particular genus), **conifers** and possibly **alpines** and **aquatics** could be included too, although the production of these last two types of plants tends to be for a more specialized market.

Selection of stock plants

The nurseryman should take care to select plants that are free from disease and true to type. In the case of some ornamental plants diseases are often masked or even accepted, as for instance the virus which produces variegation of foliage. To pick a good *true* cultivar requires the combined specialized knowledge of a botanist, horticulturist and a taxonomist. Clonal selection, already a standard practice in other countries and now being looked into in Great Britain is a method of selection whereby *one* plant of superb type and quality is chosen and all stock is built up from this one plant.

Labelling and planting

Plants must be clearly labelled with the correct spelling which should always be checked from a reliable source such as the Royal Horticultural Society dictionary, or similar publication.

How to label plants well and with reasonable permanence is a perennial problem and a few suggestions are:–

(a) Wooden label with a pencil.

(b) Plastic labels with waterproof marker pen. (Freezer pens have found favour with some growers.) (See Figs. 2 and 3)

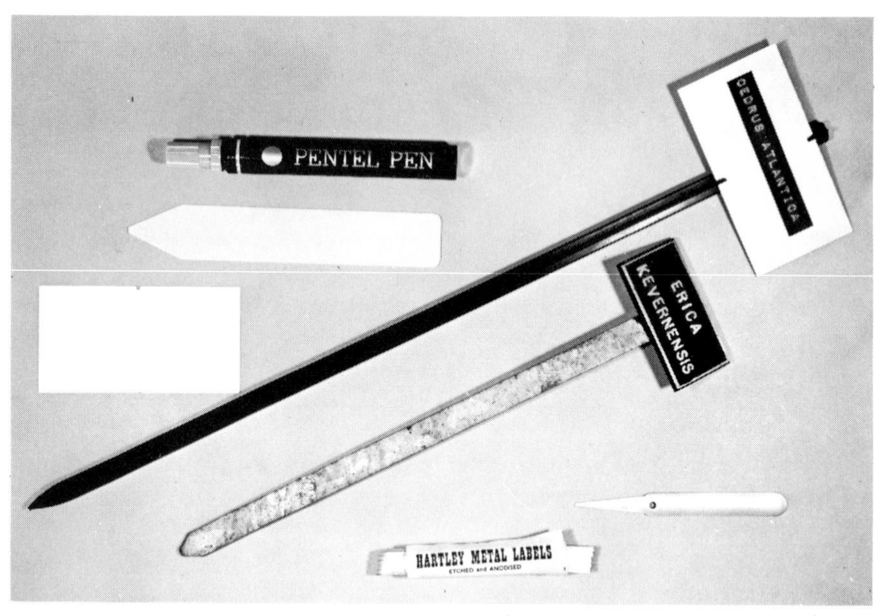

Figure 2 Waterproof ink pen and selection of labels.

(c) Plastic tapes which spell out the letters stuck onto plastic. (Unfortunately these fade in time). (See Figs. 4 and 5)

(d) Metal labels with names imprinted on them. (Long lasting but costly).

(d) Some firms supply labels with the name and often a picture of the plant on it. These are reasonably cheap to provide, help the purchaser to identify the plant, and boost sales. (See Fig. 6)

Stock plants

Prior to planting the ground should be sterilized either by the grower using Basamid granules (methyl isothiocyanate) or by contractors using methyl bromide.* If this is not possible the land should be as free of perennial weeds as possible.

* Regulations for restrictions in its use are pending.

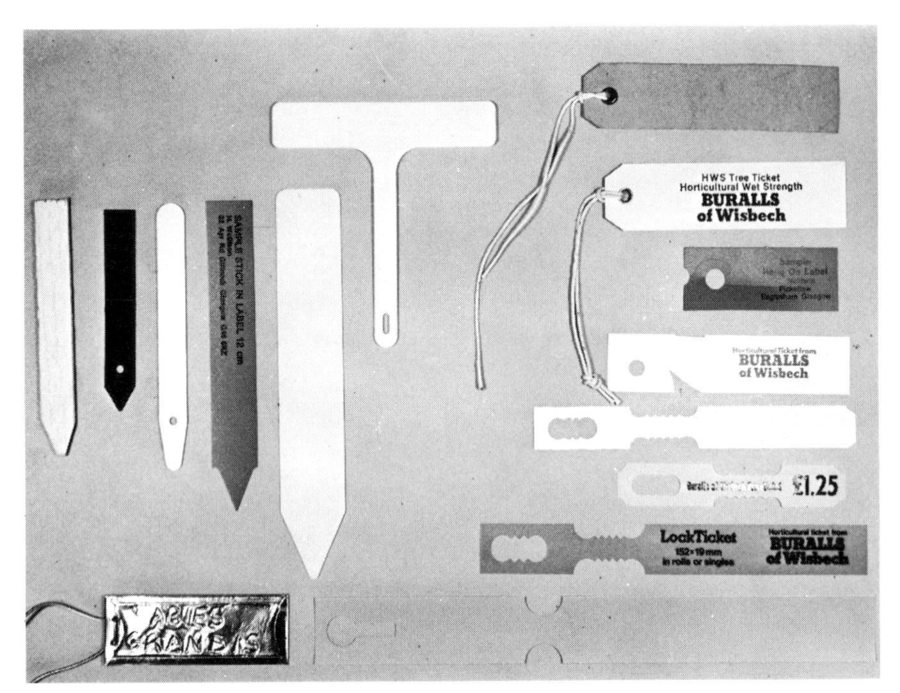

Figure 3 Selection of labels.

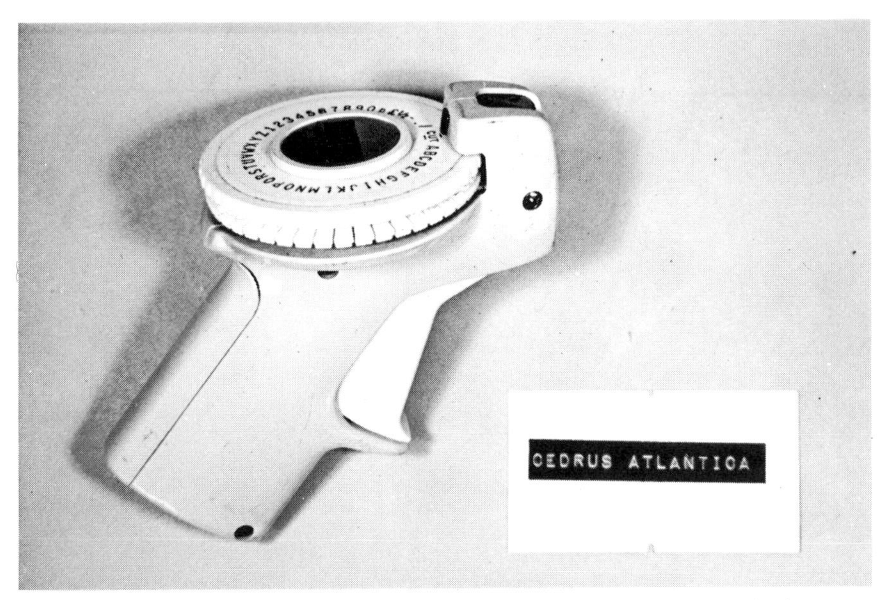

Figure 4 Hand machine for producing plastic tape labels.

Figure 5 Labelling machine for producing plastic tape labels.

Figure 6 Coloured actorial labels (often with information and instructions printed).

The plants can then be planted in a hedge system, (See Fig. 7) isolated blocks or as individual specimens with a good amount of land between to allow for cultivation and growth. Stock beds should be kept separate from the main production area so that any eventual disease can be isolated. Since it will take a few years for the stock plants to be ready it may, in addition, be necessary to purchase cuttings either rooted or unrooted. It is also possible to plant the stock plants in a hedge system around the house or as isolated specimens in the garden, but it must be remembered that the shape of the hedges and specimen plants will be lost when the stock plants are depleted for cuttings.

As the stock plants grow they will require nutrition. Avoid applying too much nitrogen as this will give soft growth and result in a weaker cutting. It may be necessary to irrigate if a period of growth coincides with a dry spell. If too much growth develops, or if cuttings are only

Figure 7a Shrubs

Figure 7b Conifers with young stock plants in the foreground.

Figure 7c Cupressocyparis Leylandii hedge.

Figure 7d Weigela Newport red with a supply of cuttings.

taken once a year, additional trimming or pruning may be necessary, to induce shape and form.

For a supply of 'hardwood' cuttings it is necessary to encourage new growth each year, so the majority of shrubs propagated this way are cut hard back so that the following year young straight stems of vegetative wood are available.

With vigorous plants such as *Berberis darwinii*, it may be necessary to thin them rigorously to induce the growth of suitable cutting material. Some of the others may on the other hand give little cutting material. Stock plants should give young growth for cuttings. However, occasionally some plants have a juvenile form before they grow into the adult stage. If the juvenile form is rooted it will give plants of that growth which will then be perpetuated. *Chamaecyparis lawsoniana 'Ellwoodii'* is an example of juvenile foliage.

Contact and residual herbicides can be used round the stock plants once they are established. If the area is not too large hoeing is as good a method as any for keeping weeds down, and is at least 'safe'.

It takes up to three years before a stock area will start to produce a good batch of cuttings but do not then make the mistake of taking too many cuttings too soon as this can weaken the stock plant. Stock plants can also be brought into growth earlier under polythene tunnels, a useful method for plants when cuttings are difficult to propagate, as in the case of the *Acer palmatum* and magnolia cultivars.

Chapter 4

Production of plants from seed

Producing plants from seed is a long established system of raising nursery stock both for the plant in its own right or to give rootstock or understock onto which a cultivar is then budded or grafted. Examples are rose rootstock, Norway spruce (*Picea abies*) for specimen spruce and *Prunus avium* for ornamental cherries (Fig 8).

Figure 8 Taxus, Rose hip and seed, Beech nut and seeds, Cone with seed, Magnolia, Legume, Sorbus fruit and seed, Winged seed (Maple).

Seed sources are world-wide and the provenance (country of origin or location of a stand) can be important as this can give variation in height, colour and other physical characteristics.

Propagation from seed is a simple method to carry out using seedbeds of various forms but it must be remembered that there will be a time lapse before the first plants are ready. After that they are sown each year giving a succession of plants.

Buying seed

The benefits of buying seed are:–

1. They are relatively cheap.
2. Can be purchased world-wide.
3. Not too much difficulty in getting them through customs.
4. Will come from a reliable source.
5. Will be correctly named (you hope!).

Sometimes it is a disadvantage if the seeds have had adverse conditions in transit, especially if prolonged, as this will delay or stop the seeds germinating altogether. Sometimes seed can actually germinate in transit and be completely ruined.

Seed orchards or seed stands

Nursery stock produced on a very large scale, for instance the nursery stock of the Forestry Commission, is grown in seed orchards which are large areas set aside for trees and shrubs planted specially to produce seed.

Collecting seed

If this is to be carried out on a large scale the nursery will have specially adapted trucks with scaffold, mechanical tree shakers and wide areas of canvas to catch the seed. It can be done on a similar scale by shaking the tree (if it is not too large!), or simply picking by hand from bushes. In many cases the seeds are inside a fruit which will need to be removed. Judge the correct time for collection, which could be before the seeds are ripe as in the case of *Daphne mezereum*, as the birds can quickly devour tasty seeds often before they are fully ripe.

Canvas or paper bags are ideal for collecting seed. Polythene bags should only be used if the fruit is to be stored in them for a short time, otherwise it will rot. Fruits can be pulped or washed with water. In some cases acids are used to remove inhibitors on the seed coat, but can be very dangerous to handle as for instance concentrated sulphuric acid on rose seed.

Many seeds need to be **stratified** that is given a period of moist chilling to help them to break dormancy. This can be achieved by alternating the seed with layers of sand in pots or boxes, protecting them from vermin, and simply leaving them outdoors where the rain and cold can act on the seed – as would happen in nature.

A newer method for conifer seed described by the Forestry Commission is to mix them with water, put them in a refrigerator at 41°F (5°C) for 48 hours, drain the surplus water and keep them stored at 41°F (5°C) for 3–5 weeks, then sow. This gives far better control of conditions as, when stratifying outside, the seed are subjected to fluctuations in temperature as well as attack by vermin.

Many seeds need certain minimum periods of moist chilling before they will successfully germinate. *Taxus* requires at least two months and *Abies grandis* 3–4 weeks moist chilling. Then, if given light for 2–4 weeks it will germinate quickly. The propagator soon gets to know seeds and which treatments are needed to get a good germination rate by reference to data, or by trial and error.

Some seeds are best sown immediately after harvesting, such as *Magnolia stellata* and many growers sow seeds outdoors in the autumn/winter to allow the seeds to be stratified naturally in the seed beds. If seeds are sown immediately, protection may be necessary from birds and mice as these will provide a very useful food store for them. Wire or plastic mesh including polythene weaves or perforated polythene film (XIRO), can be used once the seeds have been sown, and this is also a good way of protecting the seeds from severe frost – although such protection is minimal.

Seed production systems

Trees and shrubs can be raised from seed either by seed bed methods or by raising the plants in individual containers. More recently systems have been introduced which use containers and obtain faster growth under polythene. Management has to be more exact and satisfactory adjustment from the protected environment to outside is essential.

Seed sowing

When sowing seed the method adopted will depend on the area to be sown, and the type of seed. Whether it is to be sown by mechanical means or by hand the principle remains the same.

Seeds will not germinate if sown too deeply and light is a requirement in many cases so a very little covering of soil or sand is necessary, using irrigation to prevent drying out.

Seeds are sown a) broadcast
b) in drills
c) individually in containers.

a) BROADCAST. Random sprinkling, but with enough space between the seeds to allow successful germination. Lighter seeds are best firmed in after sowing as they can 'jump' up to the surface when sand or water is applied on top. Larger seeds will need a minimum of their size as a covering.

b) DRILLS. A drill on a small scale can be made with the tip of a draw hoe, bringing the edge down a tight line or cane which has been placed

in the seedbed. The seeds are space sown in the drill (the depth of the drill will depend on the size of the seed) then filled in, and well firmed.
c) INDIVIDUAL SOWING IN CONTAINERS. Ideally the container(s) should be filled with substrate and the seeds pushed into the centre of the container and covered. In the case of soil blocks which have an indent or Jiffy 9s, the seed is dropped in with the substrate on top.

Seed beds

OPEN GROUND PRODUCTION. This method is known as the 'Forestry Seed Bed' because Forestry nurseries use this system on a large scale. It has a 'raised bed' effect, due to the consolidation of the rows by tractor wheels following ploughing and rotavation of the land. (See Figs. 9–11)

Figure 9 Rotavating the seedbeds in Bareagle Nursery, Bareagle Forest, South Scotland.

Figure 10 Covering seedbeds with nylon netting for protection. (Bareagle Nursery, Bareagle Forest, South Scotland).

Figure 11 Acers in seed bed.

On large areas it is completely mechanized from the sterilization of the soil, rotavation, sowing of seeds, top dressing with sand and weed control.

FRAME-YARDS. These make excellent seed beds as the soil is well worked and may have bottom heat by soil warming cables or hot water pipes. This could be a disadvantage for seedling production, but useful for rooting cuttings. Soil is more easily effectively sterilized in the localized area of a frame. Sand is incorporated into the soil if it is on the heavy sticky side and once the seeds have been sown a thin layer of sand is also placed on the top. This keeps down weeds, deters birds and allows light to penetrate through.

Most seeds of trees and shrubs can be sown broadcast, but pines are better sown in rows because of their habit of growth.

Rate of sowing can be calculated in the following way –

$$\frac{\text{plant numbers required}}{\text{viability x field factor x seed count per oz or gramme}}$$

Once the seed has been sown it is essential that it should not be allowed to dry out especially after germination as this can result in severe losses. The crop is often very valuable, so an overhead sprinkler system can be incorporated as a good investment.

SPECIALIZED SEED BED. The Dunemann seed bed devised in Germany by Herr Dunemann relies on forest litter, preferably from spruce trees 15 years old. There should be a good depth of needles to ensure that the decomposition of the litter allows a slow release of nitrogen. This is the natural substrate ('soil') when the seeds fall in the forest.

Variation of the Dunemann can be made by incorporating well-rooted bark chips, leaf mould, etc. Seedlings produce an excellent root system in this type of bed, but it should be kept weed-free as any weeds also produce very good root systems!

Irrigation is best installed in this type of seed bed, as drying out can be rapid.

CONTAINER-GROWN TREES AND SHRUBS. In many instances where trees and shrubs are container-grown it is a good idea to sow the seeds direct into the containers. Various types are used, plastic tubes, paper pots, small plastic bags, Jiffies, (7 and 9s,) peat pots, soil blocks, and adapted Nisula rolls.

This idea which originated in Finland is a very simple but effective way of growing plants densely for a short time in a known substrate.

To make the rolls 2 battens 13 ft (4 m) long and ½ in (12.5 mm) thick are required. These are fixed (screws are suitable) onto a bench (preferably one longer than 13 ft (4 m) 8 in (30 cm) apart.

Polythene 100 gauge (any colour except clear can be used; white would be suitable in warmer climates to keep the plants cool) is placed between the battens. Substrate is placed on top of the polythene either at intervals or covering it completely to approximately the top. A loamless one is better as it is lighter and easier to roll. It is then levelled off with a wooden stick and the young seedlings (or unrooted cuttings of easily propagated plants can be tried) are placed at appropriate intervals for their size and subsequent growth with roots or stem inwards at both sides. The whole lot is then rolled up taking care if done by hand to get even pressure as it is rolled. When the end is reached the polythene is folded in and is stuck down with Bostik or electrician tape (Sellotape is not suitable). The whole roll is then cut in half either with a find saw or a large sharp knife. The rolls are then placed on end and give two neat 'parcels' of plants. (See Fig. 12)

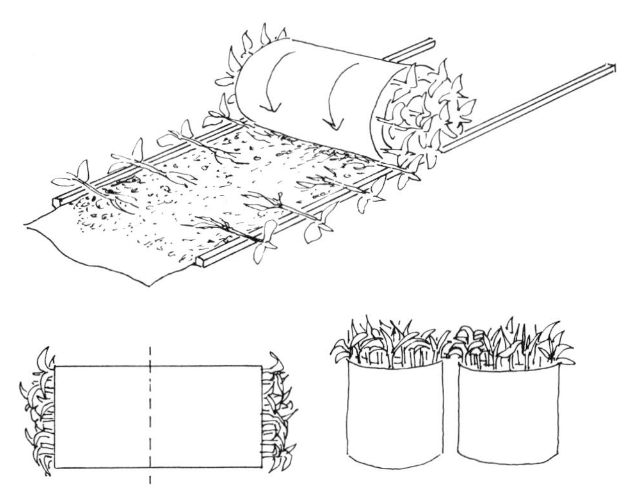

Figure 12 Adapted nisula roll.

Useful for ground cover, forestry subjects and plants which have a short production time. Not only does it save on pots but also saves on potting!

Direct sowing into containers (See Figs. 13a & b), is very convenient and the grower has more control over the environment of the seedlings. Once established they are grown on in polythene tunnels.

Figure 13a Peat pots with oak seedlings.

Figure 13b Sorbus in plastic pots.

Chapter 5

Rooting Substrates and Rooting Aids

A rooting substrate is any substance into which cuttings are placed until they produce roots and since the cuttings only remain in the substrate for rooting it is not necessary to feed them.

Substrate should be sterile when used and can be re-used if sterilized by heat or chemicals.

Basic mixes are made up and can be of varying proportions of any of the following:– moss peat, sand, fine or coarse – (lime free is preferable as lime can always be added, if necessary), perlite, vermiculite, shredded rockwool, expanded polystyrene granules, polyurethane foam or rockwood blocks. Some of the more commonly used mixes are shown on Table 1.

TABLE 1: COMMONLY USED MIXES

Sand/ Peat		Sand/ Perlite		Peat/ Perlite		Vermiculite/ Sand		Polyurethane Foam/ Rockwool Bas mineral rock	Expanded Polystyrene/ Peat	
100%	–	–	100%	10%	90%	100%	–	Blocks	50%	50%
25%	75%	50%	50%	25%	75%	75%	25%	or		
50%	50%			50%	50%	50%	50%	shredded		
–	100%			75%	25%					

All of these mixes have differing degrees of water retention and drainage. It is also essential to have air spaces in substrates, 100% peat giving the least passage of air when wet. What substrate is used will depend on the type of cutting to be propagated and the conditions given to the cutting. It may be that a mist bench (see Chapter 6) has a tendency to be very wet so a more open substrate will help overcome this if the mist bench nozzles or electronic leaf cannot be corrected. Other less commonly used substrates are: shredded sphagnum moss, pine or spruce needles, and pure water into which oxygen is injected.

Rooting Aids

To help the cutting to produce roots a rooting powder, liquid or gel, is applied to the base to imitate natural hormones. These contain indolebutyric acid (I.B.A.) or naphthalene acetic acid (N.A.A.). Some brands also contain a fungicide. As a general rule the more difficult the plant to root the stronger the rooting hormone applied. Strengths can be expressed in two ways, either in parts per million (p.p.m.), grams per litre (g.p.l.) or in percentages.

To make up a solution, buy I.B.A. crystals (5 gm cost approx. £5 in 1980) and store at 5°C. A 5,000 p.p.m. can be made by dissolving 500 mg I.B.A. in 100 ml of water and ethyl alcohol (or meths.) in equal parts. The solution must be kept in a dark bottle in a cool place.

Whether the hormone is put on in powder form or liquid is a matter of individual preference. If using a strong liquid the length of time in the solution is about 5 seconds with the surplus shaken off, so it is a 'quick dip' only.

If using a powder this should be placed in a suitable container and topped-up as needed. This is preferable to dipping the cutting into the container the powder came in which contaminates the remaining powder. Always throw out any left over powder and to be efficient take care not to put out too much in the first place.

It should be noted that any rooting preparation has a limited 'shelf life' and an old supply will no longer be effective.

Fungicide

It is now standard practice in many nurseries to dip the cuttings completely in a fungicidal solution after they have been trimmed, (5% or 10%) and this is good hygiene against disease and helps rooting. The hormone is applied after the surplus solution has drained or been shaken off.

Anti-transpirants

These waxy substances sprayed on the cuttings have been tried in America as a means of locking in the moisture in the leaves until the cuttings root and thus avoiding the use of mist or polythene tents.

Anti-transpirants can be used after the cuttings have rooted 'normally' and are potted up, as this helps to 'wean' the cutting from mist or a high moisture environment under polythene. Conifers grown in the open ground especially benefit from the use of anti-transpirants before any move, and a useful role for anti-transpirants is to delay needle drop on cut Christmas trees in the home.

More research is necessary on anti-transpirants in this country before any definite conclusions can be reached as to their efficiency.

Chapter 6

Producing plants from cuttings

A cutting is a piece of a plant, taken from an already established plant. This piece could be a portion of stem, a leaf, a leaf plus bud or a root. With nursery stock the main method of propagation is from stem cuttings, and to a lesser extent bud and root cuttings.

Stem Cuttings

Stem cuttings can be soft, semi-ripe, (intermediate), or hard wood, depending on the condition of the growth when the cuttings were taken. For example, new growth of deciduous shrubs in the spring and early summer or forced on under protection will give **soft wood**. If allowed to grow until late-summer/early autumn the growth will then be at an **intermediate stage ('semi-ripe')** and finally once the leaves have dropped off it is termed **hardwood**. In evergreen plants it is the condition of the wood at the base of the cutting which is the important criterion. Cuttings can be of various sizes according to the subject involved but from 2–4 in (5–10 cm) is normal. Once the cuttings have been made and trimmed of any loose tissue the base is dipped into rooting powder, liquid or gel, and the cuttings are placed in a suitable substrate (rooting medium) for the plant type, and are then put in an environment which will prevent them from wilting. This may be on a mist bench where they will also get bottom heat 68°–80°F (20°–30°C), or under polythene tents with or without heat at the base.

Raising new plants from cuttings is to date the most widely used method by nursery stock producers in Britain. This has largely come about through the invention of mist benches in the early fifties and they have been used extensively since. (See Figs. 14 and 15)

Recently, however they have fallen out of favour due to the high cost of maintaining the base heat by electricity, the tendency to 'drown'

Figure 14 A mist bench.

cuttings and the ability and low cost of white polythene as a means of keeping the cuttings moist. If polythene in its present forms had been around when mist benches made their appearance it is doubtful if they would have survivied. A mist bench is nevertheless an excellent way of getting roots on cuttings especially for the more difficult plant species.

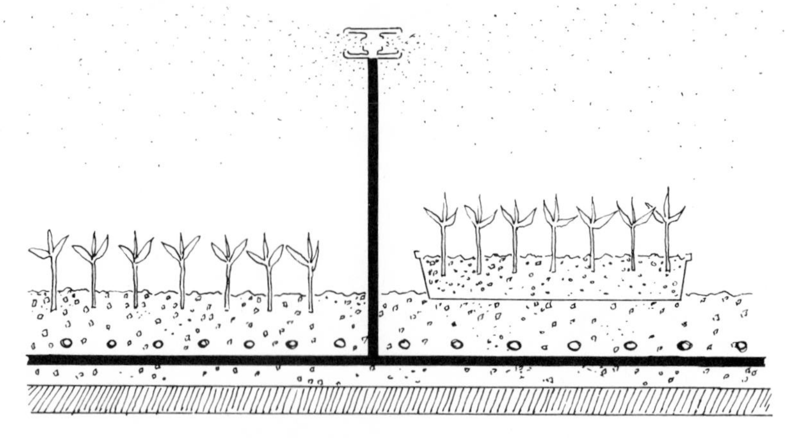

Figure 15 Cuttings (Direct insertion) Cuttings in a tray.

Taking cuttings

When the correct time to take the cuttings has arrived, clean polythene bags, a sharp knife, razor blades or secateurs (again clean), labels with some means of writing on them, are essential equipment. Check that your plants are free from disease and are correctly named.

It is best to collect cuttings first thing in the morning on a dull day and 'make' them as fast as possible. Some nurserymen put cuttings in the refrigerator or cold store overnight. Either take cuttings of the actual size from the stock plants or cut branches which will give several cuttings. A sharp knife is necessary using either a water or oil sharpening stone (to keep it really sharp). A cutting edge should be on one side of the knife only, keeping the other flat, drawing the knife along the stone at an angle of 20°, the other side being drawn flat. Some means of cleaning the knife is necessary after sharpening. Alternatively use disposable blades.

The cutting is best held between the thumb and first finger and the cut is made at the thumb end, either straight across or at a slant. If the plant material is soft the cut is best below a node, if firmer, a cut between nodes is acceptable. Some means of protecting the thumb is a good idea!

Hygiene at all stages cannot be overstressed and some effective means of cleaning knives or razor blades used, either by dipping in methylated spirits or into mild disinfectant.

The cuttings are then made by removing the lower leaves either by cutting them off or tearing – this depends on the plant. (See Fig. 16) To get even batches of plants grading should be carried out at all stages. The length of cutting will depend entirely on the growth of the cutting

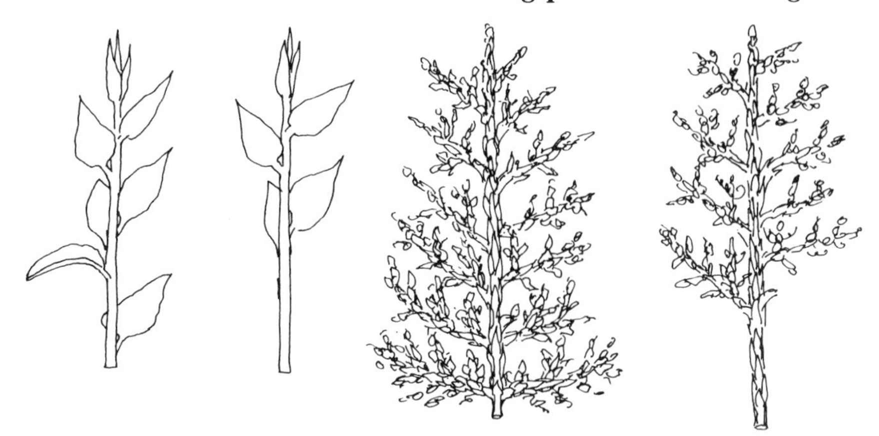

Figure 16 Cuttings with lower leaves removed.

material available, for instance heathers 1–1½ in (2–3 cms), shrubs 3–6 in (8–15 cms). If a cutting is very soft or prone to rotting then it can be cut below a node, otherwise cut between nodes.

It may also be necessary to 'wound' the cutting. Wounding is used on plants which produce much harder wood at the base, such as hollies, rhododendrons and brown wood on cupressus types. Wounding aids rooting by penetrating to the woody tissue, and by exposing cabium layers. It also gives better water and hormone absorption, allows healing to take place on the cut surface and results in better rooting.

To make the wound a medium cut about 1 in (25 mm) long is made. (See Fig. 17) On cupressus tearing away the lower leaves may be enough to wound. On a thick cutting a double wound can be made. A tool is available which makes a wound.

Reference is often made to 'heel' cuttings. This refers to the sliver of older wood left when a side shoot is torn or cut from the main stem. It is useful when rooting cuttings in frames but not usual for mist production.

If a shrub is required to branch immediately then the tip can be removed, (see Fig. 18), although views differ on this issue and it may be better to wait until roots have formed first.

Once prepared the cuttings are dipped into the rooting powder/liquid, the excess shaken off and the cuttings either placed directly into the mist bench or in boxes on it. Individual units with substrate can also be used. Depth and method of insertion – and spacing allowance – varies, but in general insert 1 in (2.5 cm) deep and between 1–2 in (2.5–5 cm) apart, according to size. Small cuttings (e.g. heathers) are inserted much closer ¼–½ in (½–1 cm). Either use a dibber or pencil to make

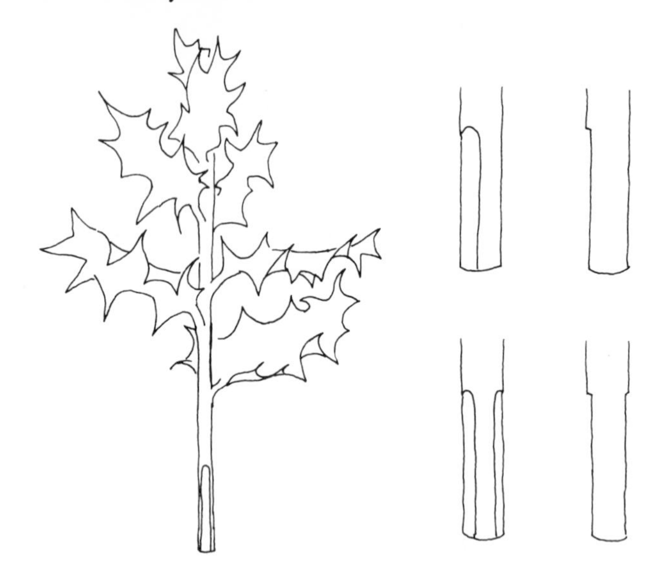

Figure 17 Holly cutting with wound. Single wound, Double wound.

Figure 18 Shrub cutting with tip removed.

a hole, have a pegged board or simply push the cutting into the substrate.

As plants will be produced in large numbers a propagation programme is essential. This should give details of the time the cuttings were made, the rooting hormone used, the substrate used, when they rooted, when they were potted up, what percentage actually rooted and any problems. All this information is useful for future reference and should the propagator be ill one can see at a glance when the work was carried out. Some nurseries define the week in the year, e.g. 1–52, while others use the month letters or simply actual dates. (See Table 2)

It is a good idea to code plants regarding their source which is often important, especially if extra good plants are produced or conversely disease arises. Codes can take different forms: numbers, letters, or abbreviations but they must provide a comprehensible system.

TABLE 2: PROPAGATION

No. cuttings required	Plant and Code	Type of Cutting	Sub-strate	Treat-ment Hormone	Date made	Time taken to root	% rooted	Date potted up	Problems	% grown on	No. of plants required
1,500	Ilex Water-iana	Stem (Hard-wood)	50:50 Peat/ Perlite	4,000 p.p.m. I.B.A. (wound)	1/10/ 79 Week 40 – or 1 Oct	8 weeks (mist)	75%	1/12/ 79 week 49 – or 1 Dec	Leaf drop	75% 1,125	1,000

Other types of cutting used

MALLET CUTTING. For an example of this see Fig. 19, a *Berberis* where short laterals arise from the previous years growth. The cutting includes a section of this older growth. This helps to overcome the rotting which can occur in *Berberis* with entirely soft cutting material.

LEAF-BUD CUTTINGS. With shrubs such as camellias where propagation material is precious leaf-bud cuttings can be made. This can be achieved either by taking a whole piece of the stem plus bud, as for mahonia, or a cut into the stem behind the bud. The new plant arises from the bud. (See Figs. 20 and 21)

ROOT CUTTINGS. Some plants regenerate well from roots. These include *Rubus* spp. and *Rhus typhina*. There are two types of root cutting, one which grows vertically (e.g. *Rhus*), and those which grow parallel to the ground (e.g. *Rubus*). The cuttings are made according to their type of growth. If vertical cuttings are taken then polarity is important and one end is cut at a slant usually the base, which is first dipped in a fungicide before being placed in substrate – vertically or horizontally according to their usual mode of growth. Boxes are frequently used. (See Fig. 22)

The usual time to take root cuttings is from November to March. This ties in well with the lifting of trees and shrubs from the open ground for sale or replanting, as a certain amount of 'root pruning'

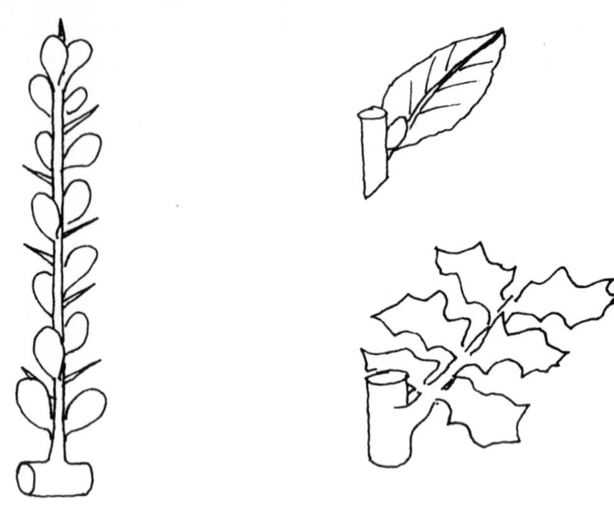

Figure 19 Mallet cutting of Berberis.

Figure 20 Leaf stalk and bud cuttings.

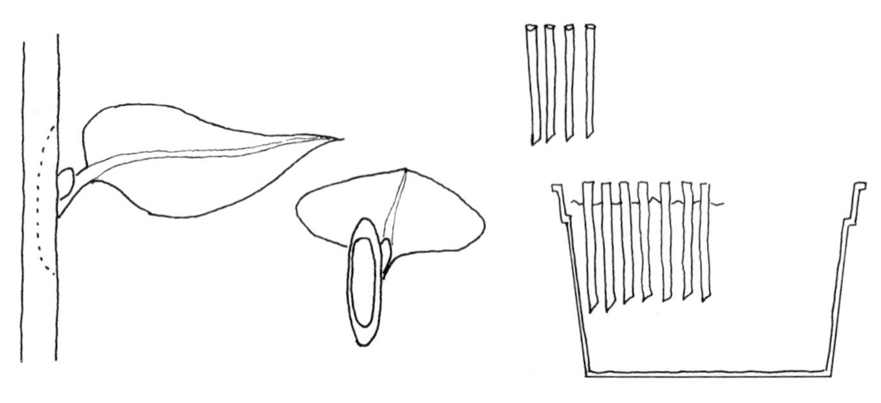

Figure 21 Leaf bud cutting of Camellia.

Figure 22 Root cuttings.

invariably takes place. Place cuttings on a mist bench or in a cool greenhouse for rooting and when this takes place the plants can be potted up in suitable containers and placed in a polythene tunnel to grow on.

Growing cuttings in individual units

PAPER POTS. These are honeycomb cells made of paper which are stretched out and put into an outer container. Cuttings or seed can be placed directly into each cell – once they have been filled with compost or substrate. After rooting they are then potted into another type of container. The gum joining the cells dissolves with moisture allowing separation.

PEAT POTS. There is a wide variety of peat pots on the market, either single or in strips or cones. Their main advantage is that they can be planted directly into the ground, making sure that the side and top is torn to allow roots to come through and prevent drying out of the plant.

If compressed peat 'pots' of the Jiffy 7 type are used with thin polypropelene net it is advisable to damage the netting also, as this will assist the roots to develop.

Both the hollow peat pots and Jiffy 7s (or 9s) should be soaked with water to either prevent the pot from absorbing moisture from the substrate, or expansion of the Jiffy 7 and 9s.

A propagating pack made of expanded polystyrene or plastic is a recent idea. The individual plant forms a root system which can then be pushed out of the pack and potted up. The packs can be used over and over again after being cleaned, but should be carefully handled (See Fig. 23) in the case of polystyrene.

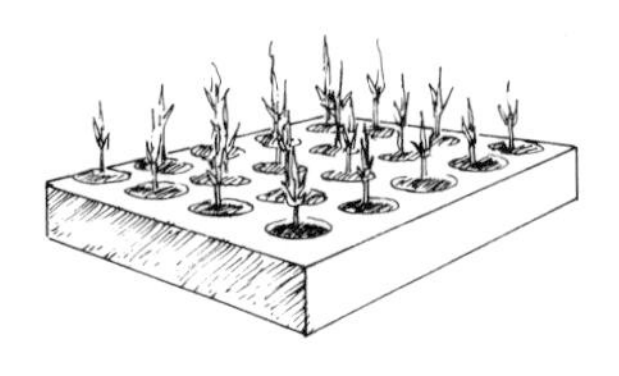
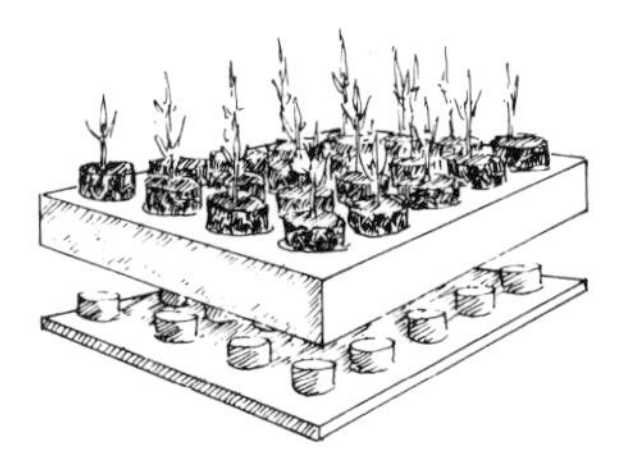

Figure 23 Polystyrene growing cells.

Figure 24 Cutting rooted in a soil block.

SOIL OR PEAT BLOCKS. Although used more in vegetable and bedding plant production they can be useful for nursery stock seed and cuttings. Blocks avoid the use of pots or boxes but the blocking machine, either hand or automatic, has to be purchased in the first instance, and it is a question of scale whether the cost of an automatic blocker is justified. Blocking compost of a suitable type must also be available. (See Fig. 24)

Chapter 7

Propagation Areas

In gardens and nurseries the traditional method of raising new plants was to put cuttings in closed cases in glasshouses or in frames and forget them, for a while at any rate! Bell jar and cloches were also used and the idea was to keep the cuttings moist until they had rooted. By keeping a humid environment, moisture was re-cycled. Wardian cases made of glass housed living plants on long voyages back from distant parts of the world.

Base heat in the area of root formations gives an added advantage in the greenhouse or frame, but heating by electricity on mist benches is costly and ways of reducing this have been investigated. One way is to heat only for specific periods either during the day or night. Another is to use the existing heating system, i.e. small bore hot water pipes, to give base heat, or better still if constructing a new mist system, to incorporate the pipes in porous concrete, so allowing heat to filter up to the cuttings. Misting systems can be installed at ground level if need be. Cuttings are prepared on 'normal' benches, placed in trays and only removed from the mist once they have rooted.

Polythene tenting is proving widely acceptable as an alternative to mist, reverting to the older system of keeping cuttings completely enclosed and re-cycling the moisture until they root.

Single walk-in polythene tunnels

With misting systems these make very good 'Prop. houses'. Here the heat comes from the sun which is trapped in the house and heats up the surrounding soil. Polythene tunnels are obviously more efficient in summer than winter – although it is remarkable what can be achieved with soil warmed 'tents' inside an unheated tunnel. These are called double tunnels and result in a cheap effective way of rooting cuttings.

A system has been devised at Loughgall Centre in Northern Ireland for plant production. Two batches of cuttings are rooted during the summer under milky polythene and one during winter under clear polythene. (See Fig. 25)

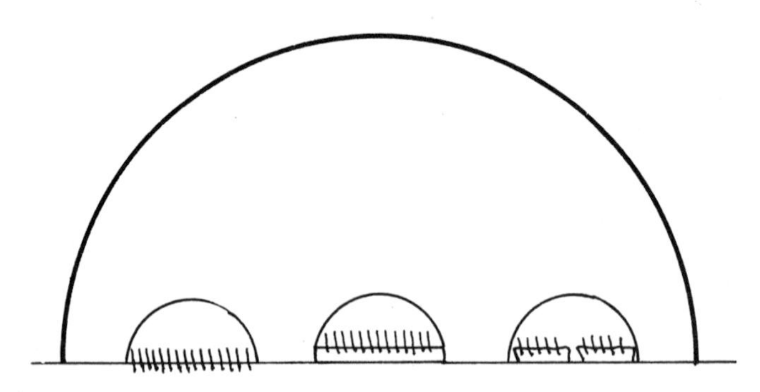

Figure 25 Double tunnel for cuttings.

Three low tunnels 4 ft (1.2 m) wide can if necessary be accommodated in one walk-in 16 ft (5.0 m) wide. There are three basic methods:– (1) Side boards are put in place $4^1/_2$ in (12 cm) lined with thin polythene and rooting substrate between them. (2) Alternatively, cultivate the small tunnel area, incorporate some medium grade sand on the top and dibble the cuttings in. (3) The cuttings can also be inserted in boxes and placed on the ground, and then covered with polythene. All three systems are prone to drying out but the ones in the trays are more likely to need an occasional watering.

If the cuttings are given a routine dip in Captan or Benlate, or are sprayed overhead when inserted this should reduce rotting or disease but constant checking is required to see all is well. And if any drying out occurs spray overhead with water.

Frame yard

A frame area is always a good area for plant production from seed, cuttings, lining out plants or as standing ground. Some frames may have a type of soil-warming for rooting cuttings and this is beneficial although it is more difficult to maintain the heat in such a structure compared to a greenhouse floor or bench.

Frames are more often used for cold propagation where cuttings are put in for a longer time and allowed to root slowly, for instance in September to be lifted the following April. Most of these older frames have heavy glass lights with small panes of glass. While the newer dutch lights are not heavy, and are easier to handle, they need to be well secured in windy weather.

Because of the heat and air loss many frames used specifically for propagation were in earlier days double-glazed or had an inner glass case to cut down the moisture loss. Recently polythene has taken the place of inner glass to give the same 'double-glazed' effect and this is proving successful, but as the polythene under the glass tends to sag, especially where water collects, it has been found to be just as effective to put the polythene over the glass. Using existing vacant frames in this way is at least productive but rather than construct new ones, walk-in polythene tunnels are much more useful and less costly to construct. They also give people room to manoeuvre! If the frame sides are in good order but there is no longer any glass to cover them, the low tunnel system works very well using milky, yellow tinted, or the thin green polythene. A double layer of it is more successful for keeping in moisture. Small batches of plants can effectively be handled by this method. (See Fig. 26)

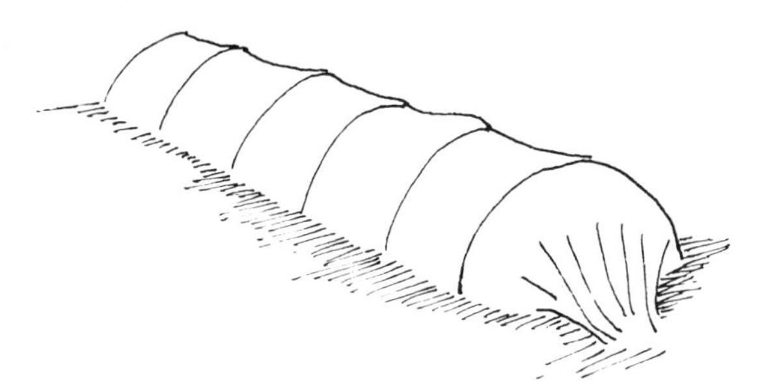

Figure 26 Single tunnel (completely enclosed)

The East Malling Bin

This was designed primarily for the rooting of apple rootstocks from cuttings. The bin is best situated in a cool shed or cold store where air temperature can be controlled. It is also useful for rooting hardwood cuttings of shrubs using the 'cooler' method. The substrate is usually 50/50 peat/sand.

Collect cuttings from deciduous species after leaf fall (October–February) using a larger cutting for apple rootstock, up to 60 cms. This size is not necessary for shrubs. Treat the **bases** only with rooting hormone I.B.A. or N.A.A. (1,000 ppm–2,500 ppm) depending on the species, for instance *Ribes* root very easily and may not need a hormone. Base heat again can vary 60°–75°F (15°–23°C). With most shrubs it has been found that the lower temperature for a longer time, 2–3 months is best. For example take the cuttings in January and by March they should be rooted and ready to plant outside – providing the ground has warmed up. Alternatively, plant in a walk-in polythene tunnel to get some early protection which can have the polythene removed to harden the plants off at a later date.

In a bin 3 ft 3 in x 3 ft 3 in (1 m x 1 m), 3–4,000 cuttings can be rooted or callused, reducing the area of land needed initially. If instead the cuttings were directly planted in the open ground 6 in (15 cm) apart then six lines 108 yds (100 m) long would be needed, plus the space between the rows. Having the cuttings in a bin also avoids the worst of the winter weather. (See Figs. 27 and 28)

Figure 27 East Malling bin at the research station (*photograph reproduced by permission of E.M.R.S.*)

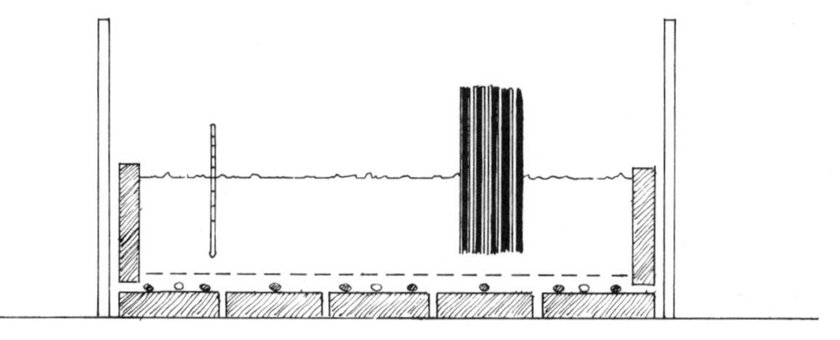

Figure 28 The East Malling bin.

Cuttings in open ground

To root hardwood cuttings in open ground outside is possibly the simplest and cheapest method of all – providing good light land is available. Cuttings can vary in length from willows which will root from cuttings of 2 ft (60 cm). A usual length is around 6 in (15 cm).

One or two precautions are necessary:

1. Sterilize the ground before use, as weed competition can be a problem.
2. If the cuttings are planted before the winter leave only 1/2 in (25 mm) above the soil, otherwise the frost can lift them out of the ground completely.
3. No soil acting weed-killer such as Simazine should be used as it would kill the cuttings.
4. Larger areas of land will be needed.

There are numerous plants which can be propagated by this method, and the value here is that the mist bench can be kept for difficult subjects or evergreen material throughout the winter. Here are a few of them:

HARDWOOD CUTTINGS FOR OUT OF DOORS

Aesculus	Parthenocissus
Berberis	Philadelphus
Cornus	Populus
Cotoneaster	Prunus
Deutzia	Rhododendron
Eucryphia	Ribes
Forsythia	Rosa
Hydrangea	Salix
Kerria	Spiraea
Kolkwitzia	Symphoricarpos
Ligustrum	Tamarix
Lonicera	Wisteria

This type of cutting need not be planted straight away and can be made during the winter months tied in bundles, and either dug in, in a shady position outside, or stored in boxes of sand also kept outside so as to allow the weather to keep them cold and moist. (See Fig. 29)

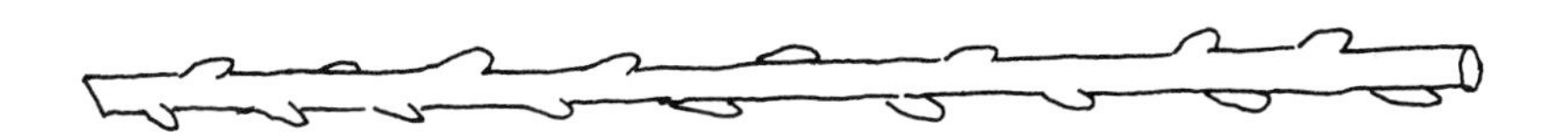

Figure 29 Deciduous hardwood cutting.

Micro-propagation

This is usually carried out under laboratory conditions. It may be a specially constructed laboratory or if another area is used, for instance the end of a greenhouse but wherever it is, it must be kept scrupulously clean. It is better therefore in an isolated situation where strict hygiene can be maintained. (See Chapter 9)

Growing room

This consists of a room constructed inside a building or out-building such as an old garage. Artificial light is used and there is no dependence on natural daylight. They are mostly used in the horticultural industry to raise tomato and bedding plants on a planned basis. The advantage for nursery stock lies in the continuous and steady light along with a controlled temperature where optimum growing conditions can be maintained irrespective of weather. For raising micro-propagation plants in flasks the advantages are obvious as will be seen later.

Many growers also use lights on a supplementary basis by installing single light bulbs in aluminium foil pie-case 'shades' within a house or tunnel to give additional light and lengthen winter days. Supplementary light is also useful for extending the growing seasons of deciduous species to give greater supplies of propagation material. New uses or techniques for supplementary and replacement lighting are constantly being investigated.

Chapter 8

Budding and Grafting

Often in nursery practice two separate pieces of plant material are joined together to give one complete plant. If the material is small and contains only the bud and surrounding tissue, the term 'budding' is used. When two or three buds are present on a longer piece of stem, then a 'graft' is carried out.

In Britain more nurserymen are carrying out these methods of plant propagation, as expertise builds up. Dutch growers are already well known and respected for their knowledge and skill in this craft.

There are many reasons why plants are budded or grafted. Perhaps a particular habit of growth is required, i.e. dwarf, medium or large, and in the case of apple this can be controlled by the root system chosen.

Disease can be eliminated by using specially selected plant material E.M.L.A. (East Malling/Long Ashton) proven free from pests and diseases and available to growers.

A special form of plant may be the aim – weeping trees or even three cultivars of apple on the one plant.

Larger plants can be obtained quickly, as those which do not grow as well or with difficulty on their own roots are often best budded or grafted.

To understand budding and grafting, certain terms are referred to and some of these are listed as follows:–

Rootstock or understock. Is the root system of the completed plant and is deliberately chosen for particular characteristics it will bring, height, freedom from pest or disease or ease of uniting.

Scion. Will become the 'top' of the new plant and may be a bud or a graft. If the operation has been carried out successfully the buds will grow out and eventually form branches.

Cambium. When cuts are made on the stock and scion it is the layers of cambium which must join, heal over and continue the growing process. These actively dividing cells are found below the bark and where possible should match up to make uniting easier. (See Fig. 31)
Compatibility. A term used to denote those plants which will not 'reject' each other and should be able to be budded or grafted successfully. As a general rule plants of the same family can be grafted e.g. Acer platanoides as a *rootstock* for buds or grafts of A. platanoides Crimson King, *the scion.*
Incompatible. Refers to plants which under normal circumstances should have been successful but for some reason may have failed to 'join up'. This can be due to dry weather after grafting, bad workmanship, or inexperience on the part of the operator. Incompatibility can also be delayed and it has been known for mature trees to break or snap at the union many years later.
Non-compatible. Unable to be grafted.

Budding

The plant which is traditionally budded is the rose. It is still budded by hand in vast numbers but in recent years a budding gun has been developed which as the name suggests 'shoots' the bud into the rootstock. The rootstock has to be slimmer than normal if this method is to be used and would have to be grown specifically for this method of budding. The traditional way of budding roses is by T budding and in very wet areas where the buds may flood an inverted T is used as no moisture is left.

T budding is also frequently used on fruit and ornamental trees. The method used is to choose scion wood from a tree which gives the required characteristics. Budding can take place in later summer or in the spring. The bark on the stock should lift easily when cut and the nurseryman will decide which time of the year best suits his propagation programme. Scion wood can be kept in cold store by keeping it in polythene bags and held at 36°–40°F (2–4°C). Scion wood can also be purchased from other sources, especially where it may be produced free from virus disease.

A budding knife is needed for successful budding. (See Fig. 31 section 3) This is a specialized type of knife with a flattened end on the handle, or a flat flap on the blade which is used to open up the cut once it has been made. Height of budding will vary from soil level (bush roses) up to 2 ft–2 ft 8 in (60–80 cm) – with a 'normal' budding height of around 12 in (30 cm). A cross cut is made first in the rootstock whose diameter should not be too thick or lifting the rind will be difficult. A piece of the stalk is ideally left on the bud to use as a handle and act as an indicator of bud take for when it drops off the budding has been successful.

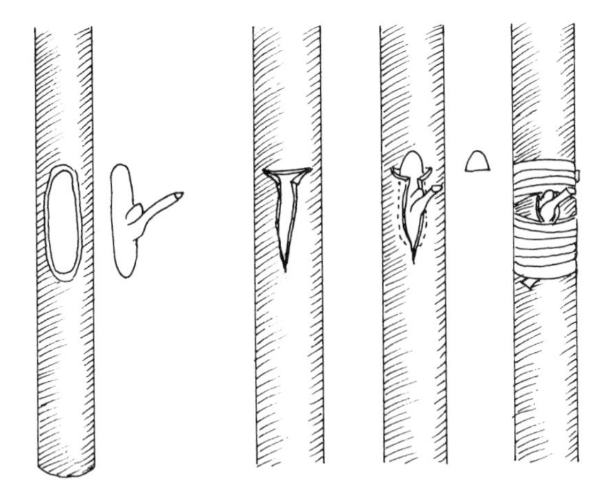

Figure 30 T Budding.

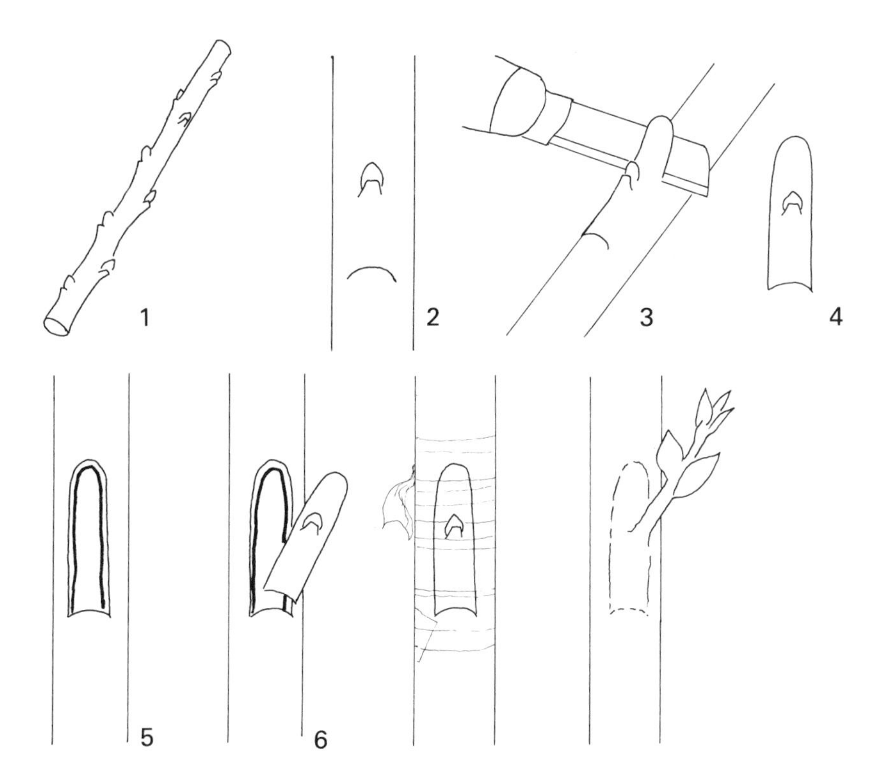

Figure 31 Chip budding.

SCION WOOD. This is usually collected from existing trees and shrubs in the nursery. If extensive budding or grafting is carried out it is a good idea to plant specific specimens to provide this material. Where plants are known to carry virus, virus-free material should be planted or purchased. If scion wood is not required immediately it can be held in cold store 40°–50°F (4–5°C) for up to three months. To keep it longer it should be stored at 32°F (0°C). East Malling Research Station, and Long Ashton Research Station are producing *E.M.L.A.* stock which has been tested. Their lists now include ornamental fruit trees.

The bud is sliced from the scion and the sliver of wood at the back can either be left (provided it is not too thick) or taken out, a more usual procedure when budding roses. If it is removed it should be done carefully as it is so easy to remove the bud at the same time! The bud is then placed in the T cut (see Fig. 30) and the top cut off keeping it flush with the cross cut. The buds are either tied in or a rubber patch with a staple is pulled over them. This is used most on roses; trees, on the other hand, can be bound with wet raffia (however it is more difficult to obtain now) or the newer elasticated rubberized tapes which degrades, or polythene tape 1/2 in (12.5 mm) wide which has to be removed after a month. Tying is done from the base up, making sure it is held fast and taken up the stem firmly, but not encasing the bud in the tying material, except in certain chip buds. It is fastened at the top by a half hitch. (Waxing is not necessary in budding.)

CHIP BUDDING. Is a method which has been revived in recent years due to the introduction of polythene tape which keeps the bud moist until a union has taken place. August/September is the usual time for chip budding. (Some nurseries in the south of England do carry out this method in July.)

A very sharp knife is necessary as a slightly deeper cut is made than for T budding. The first cut (See Fig. 31 section 2) is made on the scion wood 1/2 in (12.5 mm) below the bud. The second cut (3) is then made down behind the bud in one clean cut finishing off at the first cut. The bud is removed (4) matching up for size takes place on the rootstock (5) again 30 cms up the stem. The chip bud is fitted into place (6) and finally tied with polythene tape 1/2 in (12.5 mm). If the bud is small it is completely covered. If large the bud is left exposed. In either instance the tape should be removed a month later and not left on the ground as it does not degrade.

The cambial contact (5) is good in this bud and generally gives a high success rate. Heading back (cutting back) of the rootstock takes place in February. An even stand of trees is achieved by chip budding and providing the birds do not take a fancy to the buds before they can grow out! (See Fig. 32)

Figure 32a Chip bud grown out.

Figure 32b Resulting growth.

Grafting

Here larger pieces of scion are united with the rootstock. Usually with three or four buds present in the hope that one will 'take'. When grafting conifers a piece similar to a stem cutting is used. The scion length will depend on the species being grafted and can be from $1^1/_2$ in–8 in (4–20 cm) (approximately).

There are many types of grafts. The ones mentioned here are those more commonly used. Grafting can be carried out usually in the field where the rootstocks have already been established from seedlings, layers or cuttings, and have grown for a year.

Rootstocks for conifers are usually pot grown. If bare rooted they are grown as a separate crop in the field for lifters. Both are trimmed before they are used for grafts, by the regular removal of any lower growth which may impede grafting. The grafting takes place inside, hence the term 'bench grafting'. (See Figs. 33a and 33b)

WHIP AND TONGUE GRAFTING. Whip and tongue is the most common graft used on fruit trees. In theory the rootstock should be of the same thickness as the scion but as this is not always possible then cambial contact is made down one side and at the base. As in all buds and grafts 'take' will depend on how skilfully it is carried out, and the greater the area of cambium to be matched up (even if only at one side) the better the likelihood of a good take.

The cuts on both scion and rootstock are made with one clean stroke

$1^1/_2$–2 in (4–5 cm) long at an angle of approx. 20°. After the cuts have been made a tongue is slit across. This gives a ledge on which to sit the graft until it can be tied. Raffia or the rubberized elastic ties are used and afterwards the grafts are waxed.

Figure 33a Chamaecyparis Cultivars. **Figure 33b**

WAXES. Two types are used (a) hot wax, (b) cold wax. Some of the ingredients of hot wax are resin, beeswax, linseed oil, lampblack, and fish glue. If applying a hot wax a small burner is needed to melt it before use. Unless polythene is used it is put on with a brush to the tip of the scion, and then around the tied area at the top of the rootstocks as these are removed with this type of graft.

Hot waxes are most useful in wet areas. A recipe for a hot wax is: 5 lbs (2.25 kg) resin, $1^1/_4$ lb (.75 kg) Burgundy pitch, 1 lb (.55 kg) tallow, 1 lb (.55 kg) paraffin wax, stir carefully, and keep over a low heat, finally put in the Venetian Red to give a distinctive colour. The wax can be poured into small containers and kept until needed.

PETROLEUM JELLY. A heavy type can be used successfully on grafts. It is messier to apply and has to be smeared on. Paraffin wax allows plants to be kept on an open bench after grafting.

BENCH GRAFTING. Side grafts of various types are carried out on conifers. The rootstock *Chamaecyparis lawsoniana* can be used for cultivars of this plant, such as *Cham. obtusa 'Nana Gracilis'* which is slow growing and difficult from cuttings.

Norway spruce (*Picea abies*) is a usual rootstock for some of the choicer spruce forms, e.g. *Picea pungens 'Hoopsii'*. Grafting of this type can be before growth starts in the spring (March). In Holland however it is grafted in August. The rootstock should have been already raised in pots from seed and be approximately two years old. The lower part of the main stem should be trimmed ready for the graft. Resin on the grafting knife has to be cleared off regularly with meths. The Picea scion should have five buds at the tip to give a good branch framework. In Britain it is usually a side or side veneer which is used although in Germany a triangular cut is favoured with a wedge shaped scion to fit in it. Tying is again with waxed thin cotton string, rubberized elastic ties or raffia. The resin present is often enough to seal this graft naturally but waxing can be put on if the propagator wishes to use it.

After care of the grafts is important and one method is to plunge the pot in peat up to the graft in a frame which is then covered with clear polythene or glass and either shaded or covered with green polythene. A high temperature should be avoided (although some heat is necessary) as this would bring the rootstock on too fast and the graft might not then be at the same stage of growth. The top of the rootstock can be reduced but at least one shoot should be left as a sap drawer above the graft.

More plants are being grafted and budded in this country each year. Nurseries have self taught knifemen on their staff or have 'in service' training schemes available.

GRAFTING MACHINES. It is possible to use a machine to make grafts. These produce two types (a) of a single wedge in a corresponding groove, or (b) a more dove-tailed effect with two wedges in two grooves. The per cent take, as to be expected, is not so high as when carried out by a skilled knifesman/woman.

Chapter 9

Micro-propagation

The term micro-propagation has come about in recent years to define the use of minute pieces of plant material to propagate plants. Other terms used which have come to mean the same process but are not so exact are:– *Tissue* culture (groups of cells), *Meristem* culture (growing tip), *In Vitro* culture (grown in flasks).

With each new concept of plant culture comes a change in idea and attitudes. Mist units revolutionized propagation from cuttings in the 1950s and 1960s, just as micro-propagation is doing today for the whole aspect of plant raising. Modern micro-propagation can be traced to men like Professor Knudson, in the States, who developed a nutrient medium on which orchid seeds would germinate. This method of raising orchids from seed is now standard practice. Professor Morel too, working at the University of Versailles on mosaic virus disease of Cymbidiums, noticed that the tiny meristem (used because the tip is free of virus), did not develop like a miniature cutting, but grew into a mass of green lumps (Protocorm). Fortunately for all concerned he did not throw out these growths but divided them up, putting them on fresh nutrient in new flasks which eventually developed into plantlets (propagules).

Raising Cymbidium and other orchids by this method is now standard practice and several orchid growers have their own laboratories. The resulting plants are called *Mericlones.*

From this initial work other plants were propagated in this way especially ones which were diseased or difficult to propagate by conventional means.

For a producer of large numbers of plants with limited stock material this method of propagation could prove invaluable. Stock can be easily transported from one country to another and without the necessary

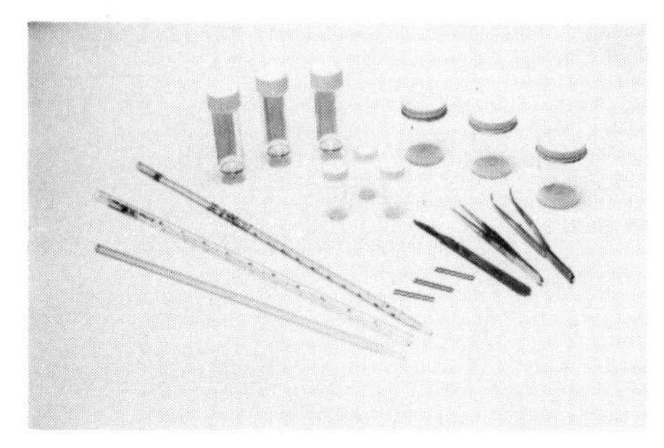

Figure 34a Pipettes, flasks, knives, scalpels and tweezers.

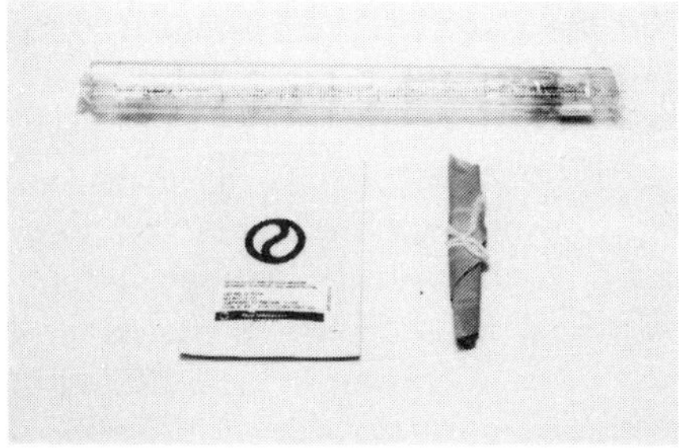

Figure 34b Sterile wrapped pipettes. Nutrient powder pre-pack. Instruments already autoclaved.

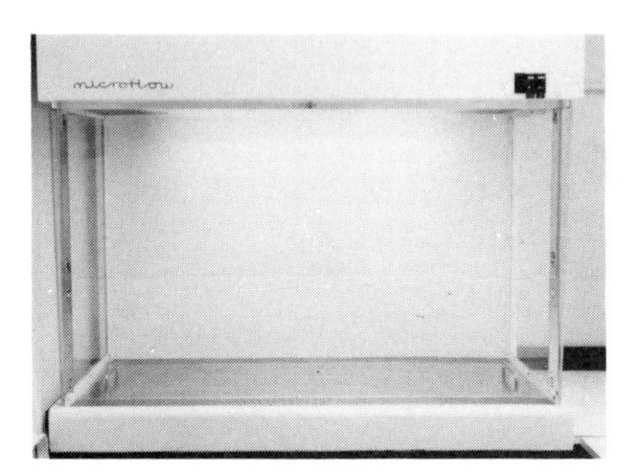

Figure 34c Laminar flow bench.

Figure 34d *Cotton wool* for swabs. *White tile* plant material. *Alcohol flasks* instruments. Bunsen burner. *Chloros Solns.* Rubber gloves.

strict control of plants in soil. From a small laboratory different plants can be produced free from disease and in infinite numbers.

Already several nurserymen are establishing micro-propagation units on their premises, or if they do not wish to go to the expense of carrying out the production themselves, using a commercial company which will propagate the plants to order.

It should be pointed out to make it an economically viable proposition at least 10,000 of each plant should be raised by *in vitro* culture and it is more likely to be adopted initially by the producers of pot plants and ornamental cut flowers.

Methods of micro-propagation

From the outset great care must be taken to insure cleanliness and hygiene. A small room should be set aside where the air can be kept clean or (See Fig. 36) a metal or wooden cabinet with an ultra violet light can be used to get a small clean space. **A word of warning** – the ultra violet light must be switched off before use and should have a shade on it when lit, as it can damage the eyes.

A safer alternative is a laminar flow bench in which sterile air flows over the work area cutting down the risk of contamination.

Equipment will consist of scalpels and forceps. These have to be autoclaved (pressure cooked), as has the nutrient media. This is simply a solution of all the plant foods dissolved in distilled water. If a jelly type is needed sea-weed extract (Agar) is added.

Most media can be purchased in packets, kept cold and only made up when needed, adding any other necessary ingredients before autoclaving. Before the medium 'sets' it is pipetted into glass or plastic flasks. Glass jars can be autoclaved while plastic ones come already sterilized and are disposable. Any flasks not needed once the medium is added can also be held in cold store. (See Fig. 37)

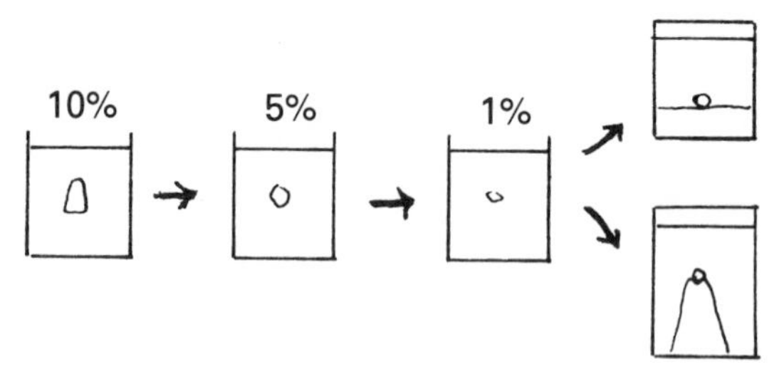

Figure 35 Chloros Solns, with smaller pieces of plant material finally in flasks with nutrient.

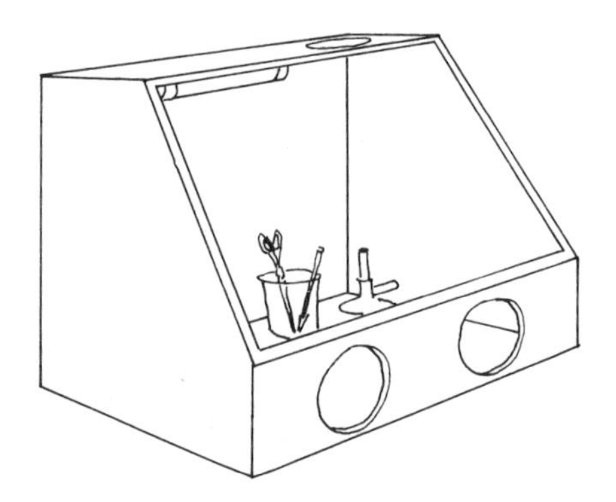

Figure 36 Enclosed cabinet suitable for micro-propagation.

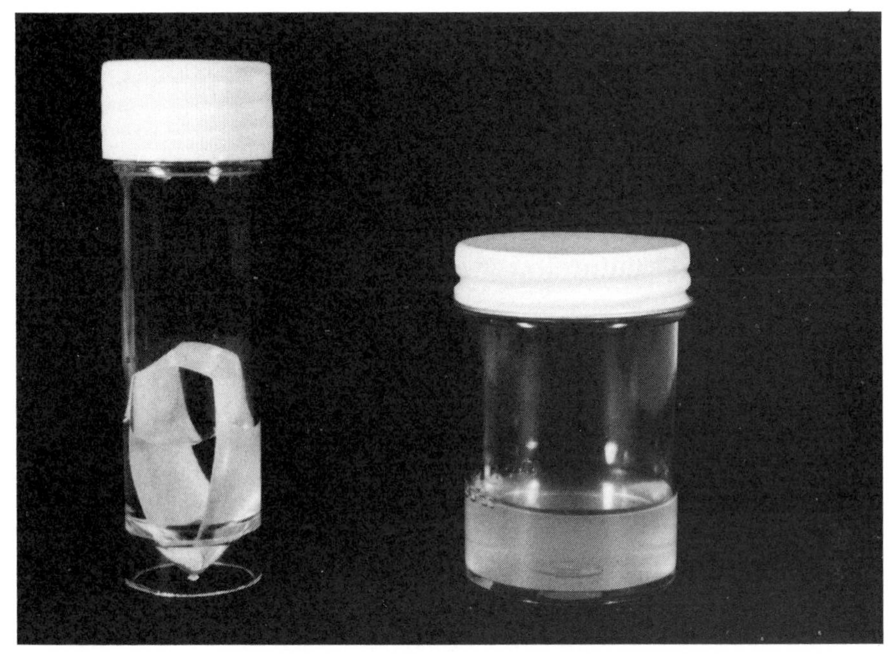

Figure 37 (a) Liquid nutrient soln, with filter bridge. (b) Gel nutrient.

Once the plant has been selected it is necessary to know which part is to be used and treat it accordingly. For example, the dormant eye of a host would have to be well washed before it was cut at all as would the stem or leaf tissue of any plant that was used. Growing the plant in a soil-less substrate and watering by capillary irrigation will also help to cut down contamination.

If the plant is to be taken to minute sections a binocular microscope or a magnifying lens of some kind must be used.

Chloros solutions (mild bleach) to eliminate organisms present on the surface of the tissue are made up to the equivalent of 10%, 5% and 1%. The more the outer tissue is removed, the weaker solution of chloros, until finally the piece of plant is left in the 1% solution for only one minute before being quickly transferred onto the nutrient, either solid or liquid, with a filter bridge. If the plant is put in total liquid it needs to be rotated or agitated to allow air to get into the liquid.

After transfer to the flasks, which should be carried out as quickly as possible so as to cut down contamination risks, the plants are then placed somewhere with light which can be continuous or for eight or sixteen hours a day, depending on the plant. Incubators make ideal places or growing rooms if the light intensity can be kept low, 120

Figure 38 (a) 1st insertion. (b) Subsequent growth. (c) Subcultured plantlet developing.

lumens per sq. ft., and the heat controlled at 70°–75°F (21°–23°C). An incubator with a fan is best but also more expensive.

After 4 to 6 weeks hopefully something will have developed – probably contamination! This should not be treated as total failure because, even if only one flask has survived and is growing, (providing it can be sub-divided), it can be the beginning of a batch of plants. The growths are put onto fresh media on the laminar flow bench with any change in auxins needed to give root and shoot development. (Contamination is inevitable and it is just accepted as a fact of micro-propagation: were *all* the flasks to produce plants, million of plants would be the result.)

Once recognizable plantlets start crowding the flasks they can be transferred to conventional growing substrates and grown on in the usual way. Often this stage gives problems and some training of personnel establishing the plants in a greenhouse may be necessary. Vermiculite or perlite make good go-between substrates with a liquid feed to replace the nutrients in the flask. As they have also been removed from their cosseted environment, a propagator with clear plastic top or a mist makes a good alternative in the initial stages of establishing the plants in normal growing areas.

If the plants give shoots and no roots the shoots can be treated as cuttings, i.e. dusted with rooting hormone and put on the mist bench.

By establishing the plant in this way it is easier to pot it up into conventional substrate.

In micro-propagation the need for sterile work environment remains constant but the instruments used, the autoclaving time, which section of the plant to use, the nutrient media, the time taken to grow on, the heat requirements and light regime will alter from plant to plant.

Chapter 10

Growing on Substrates and Fertilizers

Substrate has come to mean any material in which plants will grow. Other terms used are *compost* which is made up of various basic ingredients like peat and sand with fertilizers added, and *medium* which denotes both a solid soil or peat based growing mix or a liquid growing mix to be used in flasks or tubes for micro-propagation.

The history of 'composts' is as old as cultivation itself and gardeners through the ages have had their own secret recipes which included a wide variety of ingredients, for example: 'half-rotten leaf mould, heath soil (peat), horse manure, cow manure, pig manure, charcoal, wood ashes, bone dust, sharp sand, burnt turf (sterilized loam), moss which has been well scalded!'

In 1939 at the John Innes Research Institute in Britain Lawrence and Newell developed a loam based compost and in 1941 a compost based on a mixture of peat and sand was developed in the U.S.A. at the University of California. This research promoted more uniform growing mediums and to-day there is a wide choice of substances to make up substrates for particular crops.

Plants respond to different levels of acidity ('sourness') and alkalinity ('sweetness') in the soil and can only absorb plant foods when the soil contains the correct pH value. pH is a scale used to determine whether a soil is acid or alkali. The scale ranges from 0 to 14 with 7 as the neutral point. Colour indicators can be used to measure the pH. These show a range of colours, from a brilliant red at 3.0 to blue at 7.9 and above. If a very accurate pH reading is required it is advisable to use a pH metre. For most lime hating plants such as rhododendrons, a pH value between 4.0 and 4.5 is required.

Basic ingredients of modern substrates

LOAM. This is from the slow decomposition of turf. To produce a quantity of loam, turves are cut 4 in (10 cms) deep and stacked in 6 ft (1.8 m) square heaps, grass side down, alternating with layers of strong manure 2 in (5 cms) with lime added if necessary to bring the pH to 5.5–6.5. The heap should be kept moist until ready for sterilizing, then dried off as it will be more thoroughly sterilized when dry, after which it is chopped by spade or shredder six months later.

SAND. This can be anything from very fine sand, to coarse grade sand, which is more like a grit; the grade used will depend on the (substrate) medium being made up. It is advisable to purchase lime-free sand as carbonates can cause problems in the nutrient balance.

PEAT. This has been to date the most common ingredient of loamless substrates in Britain, however it is likely that there will soon be a shortage of peat which will make some of the following substances more prominent in future mixes. Peat comes to the nursery having been 'harvested' and is sold either loose, baled or bagged.
Two types of peat are used:

1. *Sphagnum* peat based on this type of moss are of a spongy texture.
2. *Sedge peat* also originates from years of decaying of sedges and heathers. Both are useful for mixes and sedge specifically for soil blocks.

LIGNITE. This is a newer introduction, which is a very high concentrate of organic matter which is more solid than peat. It shows potential in giving controlled moisture and fertilizers release (which can cause problems in peat). It should be used as an additive rather than a substitute.

PERLITE. This is an alumino-silicate of volcanic origin. The mineral is crushed and quickly heated to 1840°F (1000°C), so that it expands to give light-weight cellular structures which retain water on the surface, providing good drainage and making it a good substitute to use with peat. Perlite, which has been used for many years in the US is now available in this country and is sold in graded types: the very powdery forms should be avoided for nursery stock.

VERMICULITE. This is an aluminium, iron, magnesium silicate heated to 1840°F (1000°C), to give a lattice structure with good air and water holding capacity. It is used extensively in the U.S.A., but in this country one must take care to purchase the horticultural brand not the one easily available from builders merchants.

ROCK WOOL. This is a bas mineral rock smelted at 2740°F (1500°C), making it fibrous in structure. It has excellent water holding properties and gives good root anchorage. Rock Wool was used a lot in block form in Denmark where it is manufactured by Grodan, but today the shredded variety added to composts is more common. When it is used in the block form the plants have to be liquid fed. Rock Wool is a useful substrate if plants are being grown in nutrient film technique (N.F.T.).

EXPANDED POLYSTYRENE CHIPS (OR BEADS). These are used in other industries but like Vermiculite one must be sure to use chips which are manufactured for horticulture. Some are very light and difficult to mix as they tend to blow away!

POLYURETHANE FOAM. This is an open cellular foam used either as blocks into which cuttings are placed to root, or shredded and used in mixes.

BARK. In this country bark comes from soft wood trees (Conifers). When it is used in composts it must be well rotted otherwise a problem can arise as nitrogen will be acquired from the fertilizer in the mix. Bark gives a very good air space ratio (15–20%), but as it is prone to drying out, peat should be mixed in to help water retention. It is an ideal substance in wet weather as it prevents roots becoming water-logged.

Now that the basic ingredients have been mentioned fertilizers are the next consideration. Before these can be discussed a knowledge of the plant requirements is necessary. Whether it is an acid or an alkali plant, does it need a high proportion of sand in the mix, or is more peat preferable? To be able to assess this comes with experience or from reference material, as no two nurseries are alike and it may be that the type of water available, hard or soft, will have an influence on the fertilizer content, or on the method of application. The time of year plants are potted will have a bearing on the rate of fertilizers in a mix because during the winter the rates can be reduced by half as the plants are not actively growing (or the growth rate has slowed down) and they no longer need a high fertilizer level. In view of the unstable nature of nitrogen fertilizers should the substrates be stored for any length of time the use of organic and slow release types should be delayed until the last suitable occasion. It becomes even more critical if the storage area is a warm shed.

What nutrients do plants need and how can these be applied to the best advantage?

The principal nutrients are nitrogen, phosphorous and potassium (N,P,K.) followed by calcium, magnesium and sulphur, (Ca, Mg & S). The *minor* or *trace* elements are boron, chlorine, copper, iron, manganese, molybdenum and zinc (B, Cl, Cu, Fe, Mn, Mo & Zn). The chemical symbols are noted as they often appear in .the instructions for using fertilizers.

A frit, which is a by-product of the glass industry consisting of many surfaced particles of residual silicals will give all the trace elements necessary and one of the samples of frits available to the nursery trade 253A for example contains B 2%, Cu 2%, Fe 12%, Mn 5%, Mo 0.13% and Zn 4%. Frits are only added to loamless mixes as loam contains trace elements already.

Sources of plant food

NITROGEN (N) either as Ammonia NH_4 (a better form for Ericaceous plants) or as Nitrate NO_3 it is applied combined with other plant foods.
i.e. Ammonium sulphate $(NH_4)_2$ gives 21% N
Calcium nitrate Ca $(NO_3)_2$ gives 17% N, 24% Ca
Ammonium nitrate NH_4NO_3 gives 35% N (equal amounts) of NH_4 and NO_3
Potassium nitrate KNO_3 gives 13% N, 38% K (so obviously is a K source first).

PHOSPHORUS (P) Superphosphate (supers) gives 8% P
Triple Supers gives 24% P
Monoammonium phosphate $NH_4H_2PO_4$
Basic Slag gives 3–9% (also contains Ca)

POTASSIUM (K) Potassium sulphate K_2SO_4 gives 44% K
Potassium nitrate KNO_3 gives 38% K and also contains 13% N.

CALCIUM (Ca) commonly known as 'lime'.
Calcium carbonate $(CaCO_3)$
Calcium hydroxide Ca $(OH)_2$
Calcium sulphate $CaSO_4$ 'Gypsum'

MAGNESIUM (Mg) Magnesium sulphate $MgSO_4H_4H_2O$ Kieserite gives 16% Mg
Magnesium sulphate ($MgSO_4$ $7H_2O$) Epsom Salts gives 10% Mg

	Magnesium Limestone (varies from 3% to 11–13% Mg)
SULPHUR (S)	Absorbed as sulphates (already mentioned)

In practice P and K will be expressed as P_2O and K_2O.

The whole substrate (compost) can now be prepared by adding the required nutrients to the bulk ingredient i.e. Peat/Sand or Bark and some useful ones for nursery stock are listed below.

There are three groups.

1. Loam based (John Innes)
2. Loamless (peat/sand, peat/perlite, peat/bark, peat/100% etc.) with added fertilisers.
3. Peat/sand with a percentage of loam added for a buffering effect.

Five main ways of supplying fertilizers

(a) Add straight fertilizers at the beginning for rooted cuttings or seedling trees and then liquid feed.
(b) Add straight fertilizers at the beginning but 'top dress' with supplementary dry fertilizers in the containers when needed.
(c) Use slow release fertilizers at the beginning which should carry the plant through one or two growing seasons without any further additional fertilizers.
(d) Use slow release fertilizers and if the plants run short of feed a supplementary liquid feed can be put on to 'tide the plant over'.
(e) Use a total liquid feed. In this situation the plants will have no reserve of food as the length of time between liquid feeds is short, 7–14 days.

1. Loam based Substrates

JOHN INNES COMPOSTS. Not so important for large scale production because of the problem of getting loam but very useful for seed sowing of trees and shrubs under glass or polythene and for the initial potting of young plants. However, all the John Innes composts are listed below.

To make J.l (2) double the fertilizers and triple them for (3). J.l base is available (this is made up of the N, superphosphate and Potassium sulphate as one *fertilizer*).

2. Loamless Substrates

Most nursery stock producers are using peat/sand mixes. These are variations on the U.C. mixes which are more suitable for this country.

One or two examples are given but these are very general ones and it is up to the grower to decide which will suit his/her particular plants. The method of irrigation, whether to feed later or put all the nutrients

JOHN INNES COMPOSTS

Basic substrates by volume	Fertilizers	Rate per cubic metre	Rate per cubic yard
Seed			
2 parts loam (pH 5.5–6.5)	Superphosphate	1.18 kg	2 lbs
1 part peat (sphagnum or sedge)	Calcium Carbonate	0.59 kg	1 lb
1 part sand $^1/_{16}$–$^1/_8$ in (2–4 mm)			1 lb
Potting No. 1			
7 parts loam	Slow release N Hoof & Horn (if available)	1.18 kg	2 lbs
3 parts peat	Superphosphate	1.18 kg	2 lbs
2 parts sand	Potassium sulphate	0.59 kg	1 lb
	calcium carbonate	0.59 kg	1 lb

in simultaneously and whether the water supply is hard or soft will affect the choice of mix.

If potting is carried out in the growing season start liquid feed three weeks later (N. & K.). If in the autumn leave liquid feeding until the plants begin to grow.

Stock solution 200 gms (7 oz) Potassium nitrate (KNO_3) in 1 gall (4.5 litres)
180 gms ($6^1/_2$ oz) Ammonium nitrate (NH_4NO_3) 1 gall (4.5 litres)

This can be diluted to meet plant requirements and applied at every watering or once a week or fortnight through the irrigation system. If applied overhead wash off with fresh water on hot sunny days and if irrigation by capillary action is used it may be necessary to wash the top of the pots to avoid a salt build up.

Loamless and Top Dressing

Phosphate gets used up in peat/sand substrates especially if they have been grown for a while and have had overhead irrigation. If it has been a very wet summer or at the beginning of a new growing season a 10:20:10: N.P.K. is recommended applied at $1^1/_2$–4 oz per yd^2 (metric m) 40–100 gms/m^2 (on the surface of the pots), the lower rate for slow or medium growing plants and up to 4 oz (100 gms) for old or very vigorous plants.

LIQUID FERTILIZER DILUTION CHART

Group of Plants	Constant Feed Each Watering		Weekly Feed	
	Dilution of Stock Soln.	Approx. P.P.M. N + K_2O	Dilution of Stock Soln.	Approx. P.P.M. N & K_2O
Slow growing plants Ericas & Jap. Azaleas	1:400	50	1:200	100
Medium vigour berberis, Ilex, Thuja	1:200	100	1:100	200
Fast growing plants Pyracantha, Hydrangea, x Cup. leylandii	1:100	200	1:50	400

PEAT/SAND MIX FOR NURSERY STOCK PLANTS

Basic Substrates by Volume	Fertilizers	Shrubs per cubic metre	Shrubs per cubic yard
75% medium sphagnum peat 25% lime free sharp sand	Potassium nitrate	0.75 kg	1¼ lbs
	Single supers	2.4 kg	4 lbs
	Magnesium lime	2.4 kg	4 lbs
	Ground lime*	1.2 kg	2 lbs
	Fritted trace elements	3.0 kg	½ lb

Loamless substrate with slow release fertilizers

As the name suggest these fertilizers act slowly over a long period and are supplied by bacterial or fungal action in the case of hoof and horn or dried blood. Another of this type of slow release fertilizer is urea-formaldehyde. More recent introductions however, are resin, clay or sulphur coated particles of combined fertilizers. The release action in these is governed by moisture and temperature. The release rate can be doubled over 68°F (20°C), as has been found with Osmocote. The advantage of this type of fertilizer for the busy nurseryman is that complete feeding can be put into the substrate at the beginning and

* For Conifers and Ericaceous plants omit the ground lime stone.

depending on how long the plant will be in the nursery, the appropriate rate or strength can be applied, saving time and labour.

As slow release fertilizers are expensive and scorching can occur if too high a rate is mixed in it is essential that the correct rate for the crop is worked out. If potting over winter, standing the plants in polythene tunnels, or using capillary watering, the rate can be reduced by half.

If more granular or slow release fertilizer need to be applied later, an injector is on the market for this purpose. It is also useful for adding small amounts of pesticides etc.

Mixing composts

Having decided on the mix to use it has to be prepared. As even mixing is essential it may be necessary to add lime-free sand to the fritted trace elements to aid an even spread, also to break down any lumps in other fertilizers (except for the ones already in granular form). This can be done by crushing or pressing through a riddle, otherwise pockets of concentrated fertilizers can occur causing plant scorch or death.

Obviously on a large scale a highly mechanised continuous mixing process would be necessary particularly when feeding a potting machine like a JAVO (see Fig. 39). For smaller amounts a low loading cement or concrete type is useful as it does give an even mix.

Figure 39 Potting machine (Photograph by permission of Javo B.V. Holland).

It is possible to drive a rotavator through a mix but great care is needed both of the rotavator blades and the concrete floor! It does not give such an accurate mix as other methods.

If possible substrates should be dropped down into a hopper from another level as this will save man-handling unless the potting machine has a conveyor belt system bringing the substrate directly up to the hopper.

MIXING BY HAND. This is useful for small amounts and gives a good mix. Ingredients should be sprinkled in layers, shovelled from the bottom of the heap with a flick of the wrist and the whole lot turned three times. The third turning can be into the storage bin.

SOME MIXES USING OSMOCOTE AS AN EXAMPLE OF SLOW RELEASE FERTILIZER.

BARK/PEAT MIX FOR SHRUBS USING OSMOCOTE AS THE SLOW RELEASE FERTILIZER.

Ingredients by volume	Fertilizers	Per cubic metre	Per cubic yard
75% well rotted bark	Osmocote 18:11:10	4.5 kg	7 1/2 lbs
25% sphagnum peat	single supers	1.5 kg	2 1/2 lbs
	Dolomitic lime	1.5 kg	2 1/2 lbs
	Ordinary lime	3.0 kg	5 lbs
	FTE 253 A	300 gms	1/2 lb

This mix is not recommended for ericaceous subjects. To any of the peat/sand peat/bark mix about 10% of the total volume could be loam. This is particularly good if nutrients leach out as salts, as it acts as a buffering effect. The amount of fritted trace elements can be reduced if loam is added.

BUYING IN SUBSTRATES. On a small scale when a good deal of labour may be involved in mixing up substrates it could make sound economic sense to buy the mix ready to use. There are many brands on the market and ones specifically for nursery stock are produced. It should be possible to get discount prices for bulk loads and although more costly to buy bagged these are easier to store and handle.

PEAT/SAND MIX FOR SHRUBS USING OSMOCOTE.

Ingredients by volume	Fertilizers	Per Cubic metre	Per Cubic yard	Per Cubic metre	Per Cubic yard
75% medium sphagnum peat	Osmocote 18:11:10	1.5 kg	2½ lbs	3 kg	5 lbs
25% lime free sharp sand	Single supers	1.5 kg	2½ lbs	1.5 kg	2½ lbs
	Magnesium lime	2.4 kg	4 lbs	2.4 kg	4 lbs
	Ground lime	1.2 kg*	2 lbs	1.2 kg*	2 lbs
	FTE 253 A	300 gms	½ lb	300 gms	½ lb
		(Slow Growing Species)		(Vigorous spp. and older plants)	

* Omit lime for ericaceous plants.
Give half rates if osmocote for potting in Autumn, growing in polythene tunnels or using capillary irrigation.

SOME SLOW RELEASE FERTILIZERS ON THE MARKET

Name	N	P	K	Rate/m^3	Cost/25 kg (Nov. 1979)	Manufacturer/Supplier
1) Enmag	5	20	9	8–10 lbs (5–6 kg)	£11.23	S.A.I. Horticulture Ltd.
2) Nutricote	13	13	11	4–8 lbs (2.5–5 kg)	£35.00	Nasin Market Ltd.
	16	10	10			
3) Osmocote	15	12	15	4–8 lbs (2.5–5 kg)	£35.07	Opico Horticultural Division
	18	11	10			
4) Plantosan 4D	20	10	15	1½–5 lbs (1–3 kg)	£32.80	Duphar–Midox Ltd.
5) Vitax QS1	14	7	7	Varies with subject, subs–trate and temp.	£24.75	Streetly Chemicals Ltd.
2	12	6	6		£19.75	
3	12	6	6	1½–8 lbs (1–5 kg)	£18.73	
Q4	5	7	10	5–10 lbs (3–6 kg)	£ 6.46	
Q4HN	10	7	10	5–15 lbs (3–7.5 kg)	£ 7.42	
6) PK-U-TABS	14	4	6	1–4 tabs as necessary	£29–£35 (depends on size and strength)	Opico Horticultural Division
7) Longfeed tabs	20	10	5	1–4 tabs		

Chapter 11

Growing on and plant management

After the propagation department has successfully put roots on cuttings, raised seedlings or grafted plants, the growing on section takes the plants over. These, if the size of the nursery allows, should be two separate departments each with their own particular role to play in producing the finished product.

On leaving the cosseted environment of the propagation area the plant undergoes a hardening off process which begins with potting if it is to be container grown.

Containers

The demand for container grown plants is on the increase not only by garden centres but by local authorities too, and will continue to rise as the benefits of year round planting are appreciated. Open ground production will still have a place in the industry but this side will be more specialized or contract grown.

Plants can either be potted directly into a container, in which case they are known as *container grown plants*, or they can be lined out in the field or brought in bare rooted and then potted, and in this case they are referred to as *containerized*. There is nothing wrong with the latter method providing the plant is allowed to become established in the container for several months.

TYPES OF CONTAINER. The containers used will depend on several things: the grower's handling system, the type and value of the plant, the method of transportation used and finally the plant's destination.

There are standard plastic pots, thick or thin, round or square; the small sizes are useful for pot liners and heathers.

There are flexible plastic pots produced for nursery stock which are tough and durable and are produced in Denmark and France as well as Britain. Polythene bags are probably the most widely used containers in Britain and certainly the cheapest on the market. Not so easy to work with compared with the stiff pots, but potting machines do have attachments for the polythene bag. These come in different colours, white, green and black which is the most popular colour. Planting instructions can be printed on the side of these bags.

Carripots made of a roofing felt type material such as whale hide or paper impregnated with oil or bitumen and lined with polythene are useful, durable and especially good for small and medium sized plants. The very thin ones should be avoided as these are not manufactured for nursery stock. The stronger types produced for the trade are more durable, lasting for the whole growing season and eventually decomposing. Some containers are now made of recycled material such as moulded polymer and recycled paper with fungicides and algaecides already added.

In the U.S.A. cans are frequently used as containers but these are not popular in this country.

Containers for large trees seem to be a problem and many people adapt old barrels and plastic drums sawn in half with holes made at the base. Weld mesh is also useful as it can be re-used for other purposes.

Some crops need special containers, for instance Clematis which need deeper pots and if possible open mesh plastic which gives a maximum air space and minimum root disturbance. Roses too can be in deeper pots, one currently is the Rosetainer.

General use of pots.

- Alpines – clay or plastic pots.
- Heathers – poly bags or rigid plastic, round or square.
- Herbaceous – poly bags or rigid plastic.
- Hedging – poly bags, (or sold bare rooted).
- Conifers – poly bags, flexible poly, long life whalehide, recycled polymer, plastic drums, wooden tubs etc.
- Shrubs – poly bags, whalehides, rigid plastic.
- Trees – large poly bags, drums, weldmesh large plastics, half wooden barrels.

Potting

This can be carried out by machine or by hand. Even when machinery is used it is still necessary for people to bring the plants to the machine, place them in the pots which the machine has filled with compost, and remove the potted plants to avoid a pile up at the end of the line. Machines, of course, enable a large number of plants to be dealt with in a short time but it does need a lot of labour and work-study to evolve an efficient system. (See Fig. 39)

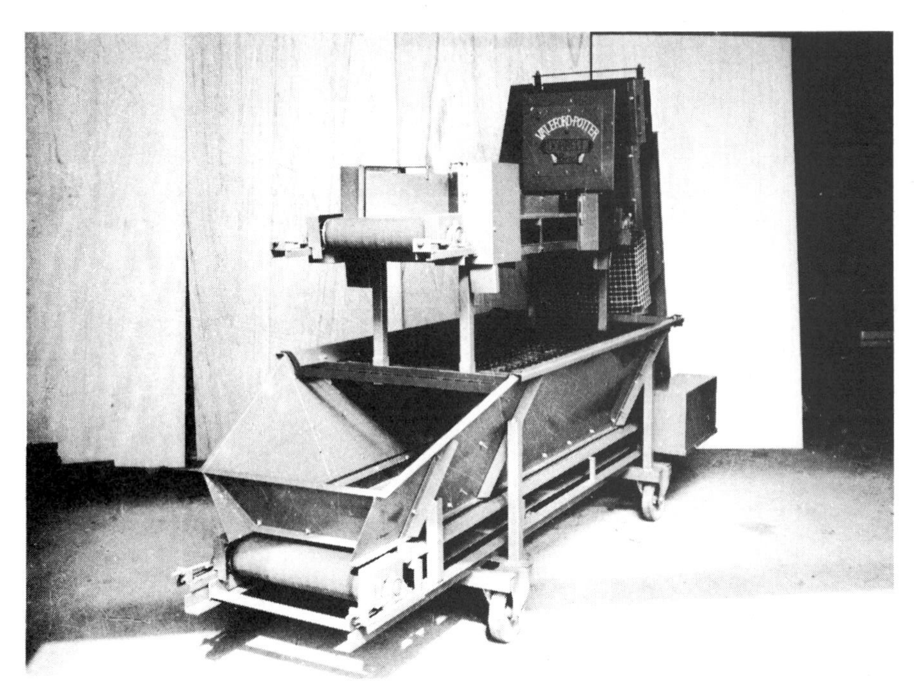

Figure 40 Potting machine. (Photograph by permission of Dorell Bros. Bransford Worcester.)

TYPES OF MACHINES AVAILABLE. There is a potting machine for a single potting bench in which the substrate is held in a hopper above the bench. The operator controls the speed of potting, usually by operating a foot pedal to release the substrate into the pot. This type of machine is useful if situated in or near the growing-on department or if the plants are still to be grown on under glass.

LARGER POTTING MACHINES. There are several of these machines on the market: two of the larger ones are the Dutch JAVO and the English Valeford potter. (See Figs. 41, 42)

Loamless mixes are best for use in potting machines and the number of plants which can be potted with $1m^3$ of substrate is as follows:–

size of pots	number of plants
2 in (5 cm)	2,750
3 in (7.5 cm)	2,060
$3^1/_2$ in (9 cm)	1,170
$4^1/_2$ in (11.5 cm)	680

Figure 41 Substrate filling pots; potter potting the plants up and placing in tray for dispatch. (Photograph by permission of Dorell Bros. Bransford Worcester.)

size of pots	number of plants
5 in (13 cm)	480
6 in (15 cm)	240
9 in (23 cm)	100

After the plants have been potted a method of handling them should be devised to cut down labour and movement as much as possible. Wooden pallets are not realistic with nursery stock unless specially adapted, but a tray system is useful although there will be a cost outlay for the trays. (See Fig. 43)

A newer and more efficient handling system is the Empot which consists of an open mesh tray in which the pots can be set and the whole lot picked up at once (See Fig. 44). This company also puts out stacking trays which are useful.

Low loading motorized trucks are good for moving plants from the potting shed to the nursery, however they do have to be loaded and unloaded by hand, each person handling not more than eight pots at a time. The advantage of this system is that the plants can be correctly spaced out by the operator.

Figure 42 Potting machine. (Photograph by permission of Javo B.V. Holland.)

Figure 43 Plants in bays. Plants in plastic trays.

Figure 44 Empot carrying trays. (Photograph by permission of Horticultural Division of Moulded Plastics – Birmingham – Ltd.)

After the initial potting from the mist bench plants have to be 'weaned off'. The prop. house may have a weaner unit, but it is not essential as plants can be housed in walk-in polythene tunnels and given overhead irrigation, thus adjusting them from the continual overhead misting regime. There are various makes of tunnels such as Clovis Lande's and Filclair (a much more sophisticated type with polypropylene reinforced weave in the cladding, and a ventilation system). Many people use kits which can be assembled once they arrive. A more recent innovation for nursery stock is the open weave cladding for tunnels. This allows a colder growing regime, but cuts down the exposure to wind.

Types of cover are Netlon, Rokolene or Nicofence. Different colours are available, the most usual being green or white. (See Fig. 45)

To get the best of both worlds, however, a tunnel could be constructed with polythene over the top and Netlon, Rokolene or Nicofence at the base, (0.5 m) giving overhead protection, but a certain amount of hardening off at the foot. The polythene cover could also be long enough to come down over the net should the weather become too extreme, or to make a 'skirt' to fit over the net in the winter making it a whole polythene tunnel.

Figure 45 Nicofence tunnel.

After a certain amount of time under a complete polythene regime the plants must be hardened off as there is the danger of allowing growth to develop which is too soft. Ventilation is essential and if this is not part of the tunnel structure it can be achieved initially by removing the top two doors at either end of the tunnel, by cutting large holes in the polythene or finally by removing the polythene altogether. Certainly this will save moving the plants but may now prove to be too costly to clad again each year.

STANDING OUT GROUNDS. These areas should be as level as possible, but a slope of 1:200 is acceptable. Whether the site is divided into bays with wooden boards, railway sleepers or breeze blocks will depend on the layout or watering system. Many nurseries simply make divisions by separating batches of plants with paths which allow one to move between the groups of plants.

Black polythene on a base of the standing out grounds is useful as it keeps weeds from germinating providing it is covered by a top layer of some kind before the plants are placed on it. Experiments have shown that the spread of disease (*Phytophthora cinnamomi*) increased by 69% on

Figure 46 Growing bays with seep hose irrigation on fine sand.

polythene alone and gravel gave the best results at only 7% when it was used. (See Fig. 46)

Whether sand is used as a base for capillary watering or gravel on polythene or soil, a certain amount of rooting through will take place. This can be controlled by using Gloquat C. 5 fl oz in 1 gal (150 ml in

4.5 litres) will cover 12 yd^2 (10 m^2), which should be watered on with a can rather than by knapsack sprayers. This will prevent plants from rooting through into the substance on which they are standing; out of doors this can be a disadvantage as the plants will blow over more easily. A new black plastic weave, Mypex, is a good base for plants.

TRAINING. TYING. TRIMMING. On account of the diversity of plant growth an essential part of management is an awareness of the specific requirements of each plant. First of all a plant must have sufficient space to grow in, a requirement which is easily overlooked. As they have already been given adequate water and a good source of food the growth will be fast and if not spaced out plants become leggy, with their lower branches sparsely covered and of a paler colour. Plants may also become floppy and branching may be prevented as in the case of Escallonia or Golden Leyland. If space allows, the distance between plants should be adequate at the beginning for new growth in all directions. If this is not possible one must make sure that the plants are not left too long before they are spaced out.

TRAINING. Initially plants may be trained up a split or whole single cane provided it is new or clean in order to keep the stem straight. Caning in many cases helps to keep the plants neatly in batches and is an aid when measuring plant sizes. There is a tendency to over tie the plant to the cane especially when a tying gun is used. The typing material should be some type of degradable elastic or polythene tape rather than wire which will cut into the stem as the plant grows.

Plastic trellis can be used to train climbers. These will take up more room and are expensive but will give a very effective appearance when the plant is sold. Clematis can be grown under polypropylene nets which can also be used for the initial training after the plant is in the ground.

Trees become top heavy if they are not in a very stout container or properly tied; concrete or wooden posts at the end of rows with metal tubes or wires between will give support and the tree is then held on to the wire by plastic ties. Clematis canes can be held in wooden trellis or tied on to wire.

TRIMMING. Chemical trimming by retarding the growth of the plant has limited possibilities for nursery stock although it can be used for pot plants. Hand or machine hedge trimmers or shears can be used. Young shrubs can have the new soft growth removed or pinched by hand after they have been potted in order to make them branch. A plant can be cut back to reduce trimming the height of the older wood which encourages branching or newer bushier growth at the base. Trimming the lateral shoots will also give a bushier plant. Plants which need this treatment will vary according to the age of the plant and the final appearance required. Plants normally trimmed are Santolina and Heathers etc. Ones which are cut back include Buddleia and Cytisus. Flower buds in many young plants may have to be removed as for Camellias.

Plants grown as specimens need to have a central leader, as for instance *Chamaecyparis lawsoniana* cultivars, but a light trimming round the base will help the plant to cover the lower section.

The practice of trimming existing plants for cuttings should be avoided and the stock area used instead.

Plant management will also require a check to be made on irrigation systems to make sure they are operating efficiently with no dry spots occurring. Also to be on the outlook for signs of pests and diseases. Plants will have to be graded and their heights recorded throughout the growing season and any sub standard plants will have to be thrown out.

Accurate records must be kept and before dispatch each plant labelled for the garden centre market or bundles (if bare rooted) of 25 or 100 for local authorities.

Open ground production

Although container grown plants are on the increase there is still a place for open ground produced plants. Indeed, most Forestry subjects are produced this way and also many ornamental trees and roses. Although many roses are now appearing in containers they were traditionally sold and still are, when dormant, as bare rooted or in a pre-pack.

With supermarkets becoming more plant conscious the demand for pre-packs will rise and more open ground plants produced for these outlets.

Advantages

It is not necessary to mix or buy in substrates. Pot and potting machines are not required. Roots will stay moist (except in cases of extreme drought), thus cutting down irrigation needs. Plants do not blow over and if put in at the correct spacing do not need to be moved until lifting time (some growers lift every alternate plant, containerize them, thus allowing room for those still in the ground). Labour costs are also reduced.

Once lifted, they are easier and more economical to transport than plants in containers, as many more can be loaded on a lorry. Delivery and planting times can now be extended by holding the plants in jacketed cold stores until June at the latest if to be planted the same year.

Cold stores are more popular in Scandinavian countries but many growers in Britain find them useful for a variety of crops, i.e. Roses, either defoliated chemically or when all the leaves have fallen off naturally, evergreen Forest trees and dormant deciduous ones. Cold stores are also useful to keep scion wood prior to budding or grafting. Hardwood cuttings too can be kept for a time by wrapping in damp newspaper and placing in polythene bags. If kept for any period, the bags should be inspected from time to time to ensure the plant material has not dried out or is rotting.

Disadvantages of open ground production

Very dependant on soil type and over the years the top soil is removed. Lifting is restricted to the dormant season, a time when the weather is usually at its most inclement and soil soggy or frozen. 'Heeling in' areas or holding bays are required prior to dispatch. These can be of soil, peat, straw, etc., but ease of access is essential.

The machinery required, plough, rotavator, planter, undercutter and lifter need storage space and maintenance and of course costs money.

PRODUCTION OF SEEDLINGS. After being raised in the seed-bed, rogued and graded seedlings can be lined out in the field, to be raised for their own potential, such as Cotoneaster bullatus, Pinus sylvestris etc., or to be grown on as rootstocks as for Malus and Rosa. Budding or grafting will be carried out once the rootstock has been established.

Production from hardwood cuttings has been discussed in Chapter 7. These can be set out by planting machine or if large disc cultivators are used to make slits in the soil the cuttings can be put in by hand once the correct depth can be arrived at by the person doing the actual planting.

LAYER BEDS. Although these are still useful for difficult or slow subjects they entail a more specialized system which needs a lot of attention. Simple layering of Magnolias and Rhododendrons has been long practised but the most commercially significant method is stool or mound layering used predominantly for the production of apple rootstocks and carried out by specialist nurseries. A nurseryman in Belgium has stool beds of Hydrangea paniculata and Syringa spp. This method ensures a good root system on the plant.

Whips and liners can be machine planted. (See Fig. 48) Undercutting is an essential part of tree raising as it severs the tap root and encourages lateral fibrous ones to develop (when lifting undercutter blades are useful too, see Fig. 49). With very large specimens trees spades can be used. Where possible a root ball – a term used to describe the adherence of soil to the root system – should be formed especially when conifers

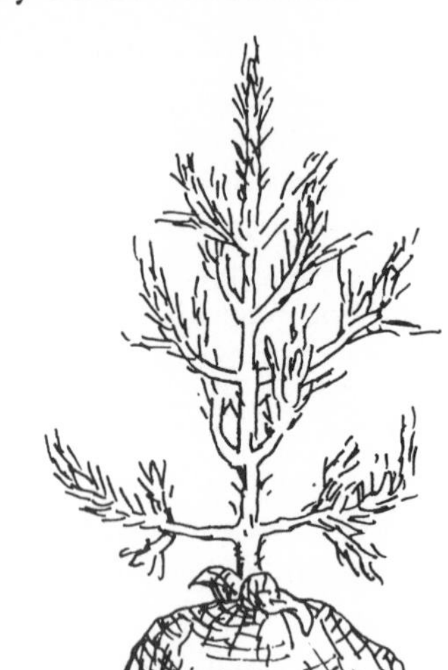

Figure 47 Open ground plant balled and hessian wrapped.

Figure 48 Whip planter. (Photograph by permission of Dorrell Bros. Bransford Worcester.)

Figure 49 Undercutter blade. (Photograph by permission of Dorrell Bros. Bransford Worcester.)

produced in the open ground. The roots and soil are kept intact, made into a ball and burlapped (hessian or polypropylene squares wrapped round by hand or machine). (See Fig. 47)

Root balling machines are now available in this country. They can be used either under cover with the plants brought to a central area or out in the field where at the back of a tractor the plants can be root balled as they are lifted. The method is to enable an elasticated net casing, fed with an appropriate sized hole, from a roll underneath. The operator, by using a foot pedal/bar controls the clamping and cutting mechanism, lifts the plant clear and continues with the next plant.

The plants can be trenched in again to await dispatch; however if this should be over a long period the polypropylene squares are advised as they do not rot.

Which ever system(s) the nursery adopts will depend on the outlet for the product and the quality produced will depend on skilful management.

Chapter 12

Applying Water to Plants

Water is around us in varying supplies. It may drop in a pure form as rain, or come from a natural spring or well. Minerals such as iron are often dissolved in this type of water in varying amounts. If the water comes from a river there may be pollution problems but the River Purification Board has strict control over pollution of rivers and sampling is carried out on a routine basis. Information about your local river can be obtained from the appropriate purification board. Permission is needed in England to take water from a river. In Scotland it is not necessary unless someone further down-stream suffers by there being an inadequate supply as a result of it being used upstream. Most nurseries use mains water which has come through a reservoir where it will have been chemically purified. It will either be hard water with quantities of calcium carbonate dissolved in it or soft (a much purer form) without excess calcium carbonate. Whether one is in a hard or soft water area will depend on the geographical location of the nursery. If hard water does give a lot of trouble then a water softener plant should be installed.

As there is a water rate it would seem sensible to put on only the water the plants need. Water is plentiful in this country and, apart from the summer of 1976 where droughts were experienced in certain parts of Britain, we take it for granted. Rainfall too, often offsets any irrigation which may be needed, but checks should be made to make sure the plants are receiving enough water as often the shape of the plant deters water from reaching the roots. A bushy conifer is a good example where foliage covers the base of the pot and has an umbrella effect when it rains. Water can reach the plants in three ways.

Applying it
(a) By Hand
(b) Semi-automatic irrigation
(c) Completely automatic irrigation

(a) BY HAND. One can use the tried and trusty method of hoses and cans. Unfortunately (or fortunately!) gone are the days when a lot of time could be spent carrying out this task. The cost of labour means that more and more irrigation systems must be installed, which may be semi-automatic, and only need to be switched on and off while other jobs are being carried out.

A hose pipe or can however, should not be thrown away! These are useful for spot waterings of a batch of newly potted seedlings or where adequate water has failed to get to a vital plant, or nozzles may be blocked etc.! Hose pipes of varying diameters are also needed to connect water supplied to the irrigation installations. (See Fig. 50)

(b), (c) Water can be supplied through an irrigation system in three ways. These may be *semi-automatic*, or *completely automatic* (although these installations are more usual in glasshouse production).

1. Overhead application
2. Direct into containers in a droplet form. (See Figs. 51 and 52).
3. Capillary, which supplies water below the pots or at the base of pots allowing the plant to take up the water by capillary action.

Whichever system is used will depend on the crops grown. If large

Figure 50 Handwatering.

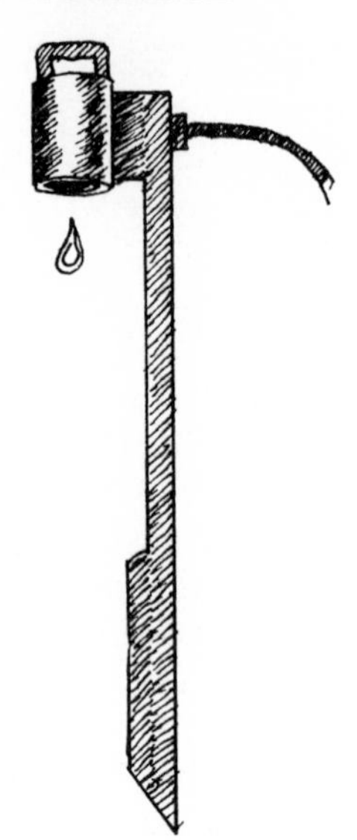

Figure 51 Individual drip irrigation.

trees are in containers then a drip system is useful. If conifers are grown where their habit covers the pots then capillary is better. For larger areas of shrubs with an open habit of growth then overhead is acceptable.

The method used will also depend on the location. On a windy site overhead irrigation would not be effective unless large droplets are formed. So in that situation capillary irrigation could be used. In an area with a high rainfall, automatic capillary, no matter how effective, would give the plants water from below and above – thus a double dose, and possibly too much moisture. Attention has also to be paid to the irrigation system used at the plants' destination in a garden centre or nursery.

1. OVERHEAD. This copies the action of the rain. Most systems except for the very basic ones, have a movement mechanism which allows them to oscillate through 180°. Others have a trigger type mechanism which, when it is hit by the water under pressure disperses the water and shoots it out over a large area either in a complete or in a semi-circle. The droplet size on these systems is large and they are used outdoors on vast areas of plants. (See Fig. 53)

Inside, a missing action is useful and can be installed overhead in polythene tunnels, especially if plants have been potted from the heated

Figure 52 Individual drips from irrigation pipe.

mist bench. There are various nozzles on the market which can be used on various locations and one gives a square pattern which is useful for rectangular bays.

Figure 53 Oscillating overhead sprinkler.

2. CAPILLARY. For this system water is available under the container or at ground level. A true capillary bed is when one is specially constructed to achieve a uniform level of water held in lime free fine sand. As the plants take up water, more is supplied from the reserve tank at the end controlled by a ball-cock. The water goes along a pipe situated in the centre of the bed and from there seeps out into the sand. The water supply can be supplied automatically or controlled from a tap by the operator filling up the tank. (See Figs. 54 and 55)

A type of capillary can be made by placing seep hose or lay-flat tubing down the line of bed which has either fine lime-free sand or capillary matting. The water then seeps through the stitching at the side of the tubing, or if lay-flat is used then it squirts out from holes punctured in it at intervals. (See Fig. 56)

Capillary matting suitable for nursery work has made its appearance in recent years. It is useful in tunnels and at the selling bay end of the nursery garden centre but for long term growing sand is more reliable.

An electric *water bug* control system can be placed on the matting of sand. This acts as a sensor which in turn can then turn on the water supply, keeping it adequate for the needs of the plants.

Figure 54 Water tank with ball-cock control for sand capillary bed.

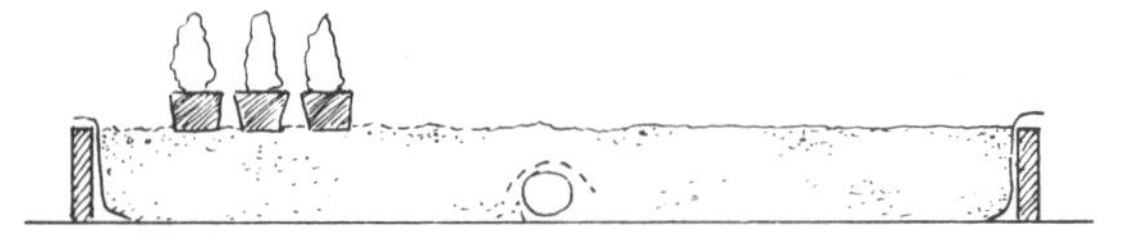

Figure 55i True capillary bed with clay or plastic pipe down the centre.

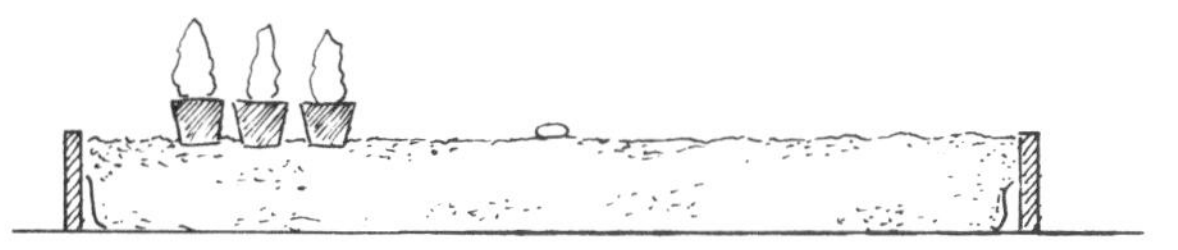

Figure 55ii Adapted capillary bed with seep hose on the top of the sand.

When installing irrigation systems a lot of thought should be given to the requirements of the plants (and the grower, of course!). One system may suit all plants, but if protection is used then separate units

Figure 56 Water supply to seep hose in container bay.

will be needed for each tunnel, or house. Mains pressure may not always be adequate and storage tanks necessary where water shortage or erratic supply is a problem. An automatic system will reduce the necessity to be constantly watering plants and leaves the grower free to do other jobs or go away for the week-end.

Chapter 13

Weed Control

As with all crops weeds can be a problem and nursery stock is no exception. In the case of open ground production where plants are lined out in existing soil perennial weeds like couch grass, dock and perennial nettle could be a problem; in container production certain weeds have become more of a menace than others such as hairy bitter cress, liverwort and annual meadow grass because of their habit of growth or seed dispersal. Hairy bitter cress has an explosive mechanism for spreading the seed; Liverwort is low growing and has a glue-like attachment to the soil at the top of the container, and if hand weeded at least $^1/_2$in (12.5 mm) of the substrate is removed from the top of the container. Grass on the other hand becomes deep rooted and up to one third of the substrate can be removed if the glass is pulled out. As well as looking unsightly weeds compete with the plant for fertilizers in the pot.

Today there are more chemicals on the market than ever before to assist the nurseryman and those dealing specifically with weeds are known as herbicides.

There are many different types of chemical herbicides, each working in a distinct way. Some herbicides, known as *contact* herbicides or weed-killers, will kill any green tissue they touch, and it is therefore essential to ensure that only weeds come in contact with the chemical. Another type, known as *residual* herbicide, acts on the soil, often forming a seal which prevents the seeds from germinating. A third type, known as *translocated* herbicide, moves right through the plant, having either been absorbed by the roots and passed on up the rest of the plant or having been applied to the leaves in order that it should travel down to the roots, killing all the tissue of the plant as it moves along.

Chemical control

Certain common sense rules must be applied when one uses chemical weedkillers. Protective clothing should be worn, including a face shield if necessary; all chemicals, including herbicides, should be kept in a poison store and the manufacturer's recommendations should be read carefully before any chemicals are mixed. Mixtures should not be stored, and any left-overs should be poured away.

Herbicides can be applied by various methods. Again, it is important to observe the manufacturer's instructions before using them, as often a wetting agent is necessary to help spread the weedkiller. The simplest appliance for spraying herbicides is a hand operated bottle fitted with an atomiser. This appliance is ideal for controlling weeds in a very small area, or for spot weeding. A knapsack sprayer is carried on the back, and whereas formerly they were cylindrical and made of metal, the more recent models are made of moulded plastic to fit the back. They are easy to wash out, but it is advisable to keep one sprayer solely for weedkillers.

Some sprayers are operated by wheeled machines which are either pushed by hand or mounted on tractors. In the manual machines the pressure is built up by the rotation of the wheel and the herbicide is sprayed on the ground between guards as the machine is pushed along. For sprayers mounted on tractors, a pump is often operated by the engine of the tractor and booms are used to spread the herbicide.

Weeds may also be controlled by the use of chemicals which sterilize the soil, an expensive but very useful measure if high value crops are to be grown intensively in open ground, in frame yards or in polythene tunnels. It is also possible to sterilize soil before it is used in containers, but as most of the substrates used for these are mixtures of peat and sand or their equivalent, this is not usually necessary. A flame gun can be used to burn existing weeds and surface sterilize the soil at the same time, but for a more thorough sterilization one should use a chemical such as Dazomet which is now sold in granulated form that can be applied in cold soil as well as the usual warm soil formulation (60°F/15°C). This chemical can be applied by the grower himself, but eight weeks must be allowed to pass after Dazomet has been used before anything is planted. Alternatively contractors can be called in to apply methyl bromide, a gas which not only gives excellent weed control but is also very effective in controlling pests and diseases. After using this chemical it is advisable to test the soil by sowing a small quantity of cress or lettuce seed to see if it germinates successfully.

Cultural methods

It is possible to keep weeds at bay by using cultural methods. To what extent these are used will depend on the size of the nursery, how the plants are produced – open ground or container grown – and how weedy the areas are.

Headlands can be kept mown thus helping to keep down sources of wind blown weed seeds from spreading to other sites. If areas of ground are not used and are large enough to be ploughed this can be carried out (preferably in the winter when the frost will break down the soil). Any subsequent weed growth can be killed by a contact weedkiller. Green manuring is another way of keeping ground clean. Crops of Italian rye grass, oats, mustard or lupin can be sown and ploughed in before the seeding stage is reached, not only will this suppress weeds but add organic matter to the soil. (Also useful if crops are rotated within the nursery.)

Using a rotavator can also tidy up weedy patches but unless the weeds are well buried by the blades may only be a temporary measure and new germinating weed seedlings can be seen shortly after.

On a small compact nursery hoeing between plants and hand weeding of containers should not be overlooked, especially if containers are to leave the nursery, but with high labour costs these methods have to be justified as being economic.

Half way between chemical and cultural control comes the use of mulches (a mulch is a layer of some kind put on as a barrier to suppress weed growth). It could be a layer of peat or bark, a mixture of peat and sand, or plastic. Incorporating a herbicide into a mulch can give a long lasting effect. Mulches can be added after potting, making the last 1 in (25 mm) in the container, or by placing a plastic disc round the plant, having a collar effect. Interest has been shown in laying down black polythene and either planting unrooted cuttings through it or if a rooted plant by burning a hole, slitting or 'shooting' (similar to planting tubed forestry subjects) into the ground.

Machines are available to spread out the polythene but unless it is degradable the whole system may get snarled up at lifting time, otherwise the polythene has to be removed by hand.

In standing out bays the use of black polythene with a layer of sand or gravel on the top is standard practice not only to suppress weeds but to cut down the spread of disease.

With different soil types, weeds can differ and each nursery will vary in its weed control requirements. The nurseryman should be able to recognize the weeds he has and be aware of how they spread, be they explosive seed heads such as bitter cress; windblown such as dandelion and rosebay willow herb or underground stems like couch grass.

Next is the choice of equipment. This will depend on the size of the nursery and whether capital should be tied up in tractor mounted sprayers. Certainly knapsack types are a must for large and small businesses alike.

Operators, ideally, should get some training in use of equipment, be aware of the best time to apply chemicals, and which ones can be safely mixed together to have a double effect, i.e. a contact and residual.

Rates of application may differ according to soil type. Sandy soils allow the herbicide to reach the roots of nursery stock quickly, often with damaging effect. If there is a danger of this happening activated charcoal (heat treated and finely ground) can be used to dip the roots of plants prior to planting thus reducing the risk. Often $^1/_2$ or $^1/_4$ the recommended rate can be applied on seedbeds, during winter or on young lined out or container plants, however, the time crops remain weed free is also less.

Some guidelines giving the chemical names of the herbicide for use in the nursery are listed below (trade names can be found in the literature supplied by chemical companies, or in the M.A.F.F. Agricultural Chemicals Approved Scheme, published each year by H.M.S.O.).

SIMAZINE (Soil-acting). Probably the most widely used residual herbicide in nursery stock. If it is used alone the ground should be clear of weed before it is applied but it can be mixed with paraquat (contact) killing off surface weeds and having a residual effect. Simazine is very good for keeping areas of the nursery clean, pathways, and areas between established plants. On younger stock, some plants may be susceptible to damage and reference can be made to plants which will not tolerate simazine in the M.A.F.F. Short Term Leaflet, No. 69 'Weed Control in Nursery Stock Production'. (Details of other chemicals are also listed.)

Often the recommended rate can be reduced to give effective control cutting down the damage and reducing the cost of the chemical.

CHLORPROPHAM (Soil-acting). Is good in controlling chickweed and knotgrass and is useful on standing out and rootstock areas. Can be applied as a winter herbicide and can also be mixed with Linuron.

LINURON (Contact and soil-acting). Capable of eradicating large weeds but will have no effect on annual nettle, groundsel and speedwell.

GLYPHOSATE (Translocated). Excellent as a total weed control and best applied to fallow ground where the weeds are actually growing or on large established stock. Great care is required in young nursery areas. It will control couch grass as does Dalapon (translocated) and Propyzamide (soil-acting).

ATRAZINE (Soil-acting). Useful in the production of roses but not so suitable for general nursery stock although approved for forest trees.

LENACIL (Soil-acting). Acts as a pre-emergence weedkiller and is suitable for the eradication of annual weeds. Good so long as the solubility is low. If high rainfall comes after its application damage can occur to the plants as the herbicide is quickly washed down to the root area.

PROPYZAMIDE (Soil-acting). Will control grasses and broad leaved weeds in ornamental trees, shrubs and forestry subjects.

DIURON (Soil-acting). Can be applied on its own or in a mixture to give total weed control, or is selective for annual weeds. It is best not to plant up ground which has been treated for a year. Diuron is effective long term on lined out nursery stock.

DALAPON (Translocated). Useful on its own or in mixes, will deal with couch grass. Can be usefully applied prior to planting and in already established trees and shrubs in the nursery.

PROPACHLOR (Soil-acting). In granular form is useful on lined out shrubs (but not so successful as other herbicides).

DICHLOBENIL (Soil-acting). As granules can be used round trees and shrubs before growth starts. It is also possible to incorporate granules into a mulch of peat or fine sand placing this on the top 1 in (25 mm) of container plants.

CHLOROXURON (Soil-acting). Gives good control of liverwort in containers (an increasing problem in this method of plant production). Also effective on annual nettle, chickweed, groundsel and shepherds purse. However, as some plants may be damaged it is necessary to keep these isolated: berberis, cotoneaster and rhododendron are likely to be affected. After application of the herbicide it is necessary to spray over the foliage again with water to avoid damage to the foliage.

TRIFLURALIN (Soil-acting). Used as a pre-planting herbicide, has found favour in France and U.S.A. and is beginning to be used in the U.K. The growth rate on ericas can be slowed down if planted in treated ground.

DIPHENAMID (Soil-acting). In forestry Diphenamid can be applied to seed-beds immediately after sowing or once the seedlings are fully emerged as damage may occur at the in-between stage.

CHLORTHAL-DIMETHYL (Soil-acting). Can be used after planting ornamentals.

The eradication of weeds may not be easy or cheap to carry out but if the problem can be conquered then not only is the nursery a cleaner place but the look and quality of the plants produced in it should be better.

Chapter 14

Pests and diseases

All crops are subject to pests and diseases. How badly crops are infected will depend on the grower's awareness to the problems and his ability to deal with them as quickly as possible. Certainly, prevention is better than cure and a hygienic approach should be adopted at all stages of production. Ground can be sterilized, cuttings dipped in a fungicide as a matter of routine and spraying over at the first signs of disease or pests. Other precautions include using fresh substrate and sterilizing any substrate which has been previously used; burning old rotting boxes, washing plastics in disinfectant, dipping wooden boxes in preservative and keeping the mist bench and the whole area of the nursery clean; headlands free of weeds, compost heaps properly managed, bonfires lit from time to time etc.

Pests

Vandal

A new breed of pest probably more prevalent in towns but known also to cause damage to nurseries. Mostly by snapping off branches, pulling up plants and throwing stones through glasshouses. Cure – no immediate cure except education in the amount of care and trouble which is necessary to grow plants, or by involving the culprits in repairing the damage or paying for it.

Deer

These can cause a lot of damage if left to browse, for they will eat the tops of young plants and the bark of trees. If deer pose a constant problem deer fences will have to be erected or the animals shot.

Hares and Rabbits

Hares are more in evidence but rabbits are appearing again. These animals cause extensive damage, cutting clean through the tops of plants, gnawing the stems both of succulent plants and in winter, of older wood as well. The stems of plants must be painted so that the animal cannot reach above the repellent, as it will eat any part of the plant which has not been painted. Guards can be used on trees already planted in position but they are very expensive to use in large numbers. Seed beds can be protected by either constructing them with wire underneath or completely enclosing the seed bed area with adequate fencing.

Mice and Rats

In winter these animals will move from buildings into nursery tunnels and greenhouses. They can cause havoc with seeds being stratified, or those already sown, and rats will eat the roots of young seedlings. There are several poisons on the market (some are effective only on rats and not mice) which can be used as bait. If there are only one or two mice, the old mousetrap can be used and there is something to be said for a prowling nursery cat.

Birds

Fine as our feathered friends are, anyone who has seen Bullfinches demolish blossom buds of Malus and Prunus or relish chip buds like a gourmet may have second thoughts about them. Seed collection can often be a disaster if the birds have found the delicacies of the berries and arrived before you have. For this reason many fruits are collected before they are fully ripe. Also when seed is stratified or sown birds can be a nuisance. Netting, either plastic or wire can be put over seed bed areas and bird scarers could be used but are more likely to be used on vegetable crops.

On the credit side birds do eat a lot of larvae and adult insects, but on balance it is safer to kill these by spraying the crop.

Squirrels

These can be a problem in some areas especially where there are large trees. They will chew the bark of plants and collect nuts.

Moles

Not only do these animals make unsightly mole holes, but they can cause unearthing of plants and they will also eat roots. Moles can be smoked out by the nurseryman but if they are present in large numbers it would be better to enlist the help of the mole catcher.

Insects

This term is applied to lots of creepy crawlies not truly insects. They cause injury to plants both as larvae and as adults by eating the tissue and by sucking juices of the plants. This can lead to a secondary infection by bacteria or virus entering the wounds.

Populations can build up very rapidly as most insects have short life cycles, and often it is their vast numbers which cause the damage. Some insects, like the aphid, are named after the particular plant they infest, for instance the Douglas Fir aphid, Sitka Spruce aphid etc. The common greenfly will attack Camellias, Hydrangeas and Lonicera, while other 'suckers' are *leafhoppers*, *sawflies*, *thrips* and scale insects.

To control these insects systemic insecticides can be sprayed on the plant or the soil. Several applications may be necessary to wipe out successive generations as often the eggs are immune. The larvae stage of butterflies and moths (caterpillars) can be choked out by dusting with powdered insecticides, or if few in number, picked off by hand. The larvae of flies often burrow into leaves leaving roads or discolouration of leaves as for instance the Holly leaf miner. This type of insect is known as a leaf miner and can be controlled often by gamma H.C.H. or diazinon. (See below.)

Other common insects are:

SCALE INSECTS, which seem to stick like glue and suck the sap of the plant. They can cause yellowing or browning as well as mis-shapen leaves or needles on some trees like the Beech, Juniper, Willow and Yew. Tar oil may be used on trees and shrubs that will tolerate this substance, but these insects are not easy to control because of the way in which they are attached to the plant. Malathion can be used at two weekly intervals to catch emerging scales.

VINE WEEVIL. These will attack plants other than vine and are notorious for taking bites out of Rhododendron leaves, while the larvae go for the roots. Plants damaged by vine weevil larvae are on the increase and a yellowing of leaves is a sign that the grubs are present. Aldrin incorporated into the potting compost or sprayed on should prove to be effective in controlling these insects.

SCIARID FLY. These are troublesome on peat/sand mixes, noticeable on boxes of cuttings and young potted nursery stock such as *Acer palmatum* and they will also eat the roots of plants. Organophosphorus compounds put into the potting mix should help but it should be backed up with an insecticide spray suitable for the plant.

MITES. These creatures differ from insects in having eight legs and no antennae. They are smaller and just visible and occasionally they are coloured. Spider mites which are red damage conifers by sucking, and all mites again can cause damage if allowed to build up numbers on plants.

GALLS. These are caused by G. wasp midge, sawfly and adelgids and reveal the presence of these insects. Some examples are the Oak gall wasp or Pineapple gall on spruce, made by adelgids.

ADELGIDS (related to aphis). These insects attack conifers causing galls, or cause yellowing. H.C.H. can be sprayed if trees are infected.

NEMATODES, commonly Eelworms. These are very resistant to chemicals and although actual nursery stock plants may not be infected, the numbers can build up so much on other crops that spread is possible. Eelworm can also spread virus by their sucking action. Their resting stage can be a cyst which can remain inactive but alive for many years. Many countries do not allow nursery stock to be grown on land infested by the potato cyst eelworm (P.C.E.) and if a grower is exporting ground plants, the land where the plants are growing must be free of P.C.E. There is also a variety of this insect known as stem eelworm which attacks the leaves of Hydrangea and a rarely known Root-lesion eelworm which attacks the roots of Clematis.

Diseases

These are caused by bacteria, fungi, virus and in some cases by excess or lack of minerals, adverse growing conditions, strong winds, salt sprays, high humidity etc. Most diseases in plants are due to the first three items mentioned and the grower should be aware of problems arising from these, taking steps to avoid or correct the situation.

All three groups can enter the plant at any stage affecting roots, stem, leaves and flowers. Sometimes they will appear after a plant has been weakened or damaged and some require a host to spread them, for instance a virus can be transmitted by aphis, and the fungus of Dutch Elm disease can be spread by Elm bark beetle which in turn are carried by car tyres and are quickly spread to other parts of the country.

1) Bacteria

These minute micro-organisms are present all around us and whereas some are beneficial, others are harmful. Bacteria live on both live tissue and dead material and the principal disease they cause is *Fire blight* (Erwinia amylovora) a devastating disease in commercial Apple and Pear Orchards which gives the appearance of the trees having indeed been burnt. Ornamental plants which suffer are *Prunus triloba*, Hawthorn

(Crataegus), Rowan (Sorbus) and Pyrus (Pear). Fire blight can be controlled at blossom time with sprays of zineb, infected branches should be cut off or burned and the disease reported to the M.A.F.F.* Too high rates of fertilizer should be avoided as this makes plants more susceptible.

CROWN GALL. (*Agro bacterium tumifaciens*). (Not to be confused with the galls caused by insects etc.) Again an unsightly disease but one which causes little damage. Some of the plants infected, are Rose giving a root gall and also Rhododendron and Araucaria.

BACTERIAL LEAF SPOT is caused by *Xanthomonas pruni* on common Laurel (*Prunus laurocerasus*) and Shot Hole on *Prunus serrulata*.

2) Fungi

These are the prime cause of disease on plants. They are spread by spores which grow into rod-like structures (Mycelia) which ramify their way through the tissue. Fungi have different resting stages: the round *Selerotia* which allows the fungus to remain dormant during unfavourable conditions, and the string-like *Rhizomorphs* structure. Fungi cause:

DAMPING-OFF. The seedlings may not appear, collapse once germinated, or be stunted due to roots being infected.

Fungi which can cause these effects are *Pythium*, *Rhizoctonia solani* and *Fusarium*. Soil sterilization is recommended, also good control of weeds, sowing seeds at the correct time and avoid too alkaline a pH or a neutral one. This type of fungi thrive at temperatures between 60°–80°F (15°–30°C).

GREY MOULD (*Botrytis cinerea*). This also attacks the seedling of nursery stock, some more so than others, especially Japanese Cedar (*Cryptomeria japonica*), Sitka spruce (*Picea sitchensis*), Western Hemlock (*Tsuga heterophylla*), Japanese Larch (*Larix kaempferi*), syn. *leptolepis*, Scots Pine (*Pinus sylvestris*) and European Larch (*Larix decidua*). As all of these except for *Cryptomeria*, which can be grown easily from cuttings, are grown from seed, control is important so a suitable fungicide such as Captan or Benlate must be applied at two week intervals.

POWDERY MILDEW. (*Microsphaera quercina*). This occurs on Oak and (*Uncinular aceris*) on Sycamore, and can be clearly seen as a white surface on leaves. Its presence can also cause poor growth of leaves which will

* *See appendix*

eventually die. A spray of Dinocap or Benlate can be applied on small trees.

WILT. (*Verticillium albo-atrum*). This fungus attacks a wide range of nursery stock some of which are Catalpha, Cercis, Cherry laurel, Cotinus, Eleagnus, Magnolia, Norway and Red Maples, Rhus, Rose, Syringa, Tilia and on Elm, producing effects similar to Dutch Elm Disease.

DUTCH ELM DISEASE *(Ceratocystis ulmi)*. Although this can be found on old Elms it can strike young trees too. As no sure control is as yet possible, emphasis is placed on the production of resistant Elms to this devastating disease, failing this one must plant other trees in their place. This disease causes the leaves to turn brown and whole branches to die from the top of the trees. The fungus is spread by Elm bark beetles *(Scolytus multistriatus* and *Hylurgopinus rufipes)* and trees quickly die. It is a recent disease in Britain but has already caused massive deaths in this country, on the continent and in the U.S.A.

WITCHES BROOM (*Taphrina*) is one of the fungi which causes distortions on woody plants. On birch it is known as *T. betulina*. Growths give a bird's nest effect and propagators have used witches broom to produce dwarf forms of the trees. It is not a devastating disease but an unsightly one.

WILT OF CHERRIES (*Prunus*) and Roses (*Cylindrocladium scoparium*). This disease causes damage to *Prunus* by causing shoot wilt, and fungicide treatment is necessary. Benlate or Delsene M which is used on cereals has proved to be effective.

RHODODENDRON BUD BLAST (*Pycnostysanus azaleae*). This disease is associated with leaf hoppers and is spread by them. The buds and shoots turn brown stopping the plants from flowering and the diseased plant must be sprayed with Malathion in August/September to kill off the leaf hoppers.

Camellias, Rhododendrons, Cupressus, *Chamaecyparis lawsoniana*, Junipers and Pinus are infected by *Pestalotiopsis funerea* which can cause dieback and also acts as a parasite. It can be controlled by good hygiene, dipping cuttings in Benlate and by spraying plants with Benlate or Rovral.

This next fungi group is one of the most devastating in nursery stock and costly to control.

PHYTOPHTHORA. There are seven species of this disease but the worst one is *P. cinnamomi* and to a lesser extent *P. cactorum* (collar rot on

Rhododendrons) and *P. cryptogea* (stunting effect).

P. cinnamomi infects far more plants than was first supposed. The known groups were Chamaecyparis, Rhododendrons and Ericas. Other plants the fungus has been isolated from in the U.K. are *Abies fraseri* and *A. grandis*, *Azalea* sp. *Calluna vulgaris*, *Cornus*, *X Cupressocyparis leylandii*, *Daboecia*, *Eucryphia glutinosa*, *Fagus sylvatica*, *Hebe pagei*, *Juniperus*, *Picea abies*, *P. sitchensis*, *Pieris japonica*, *Pinus sylvestris*, *Pseudotsuga menziesii* and *Taxus baccata*.

The fungus thrives in soil moisture and a high temperature 77°–86°F (25°–30°C). Once the fungus becomes established on a plant it is very easy to see the effects, a Chamaecyparis for instance will have a dried out look, will feel brittle to the touch and have a lighter colour than normal. The disease is spread by contaminated soil and by plants being moved from place to place. Plants can be infected for a while before the signs show, and resting spores of this fungus will also remain in the soil up to six years. To control this disease one must be on the outlook for plants showing signs of the disease, dig out and burn any suspects (if they look poor quality it is a good idea to burn them anyway even if it is not Phytophthora). Avoid placing plants in situations which will spread the fungus, putting container plants down on polythene where moisture will gather at the base and with open ground production avoid badly drained areas and make sure implements are well cleaned after use.

Substrates and soil can be treated with etridiazole (Aaterra) mixed into the substrate:

<table>
<tr><td>Loam based
(for young plants)</td><td>75 g/m^3 (2 oz/yd^3)</td><td rowspan="2">mix with 10 to 20 times the volume of sand to help mix the chemical thoroughly.</td></tr>
<tr><td>Peat/Sand
Peat Bark
(for Chamaecyparis lawsoniana cultivars)</td><td>180 g/m^3 ($4^1/_2$ oz/yd^3)</td></tr>
</table>

or as a drench:

<table>
<tr><td>On young plants</td><td>5 g/m^2 in 5–10 litres† of water (1 lb/100 yd^2 in 100–200 gal. of water)</td><td rowspan="2">May be applied again four weeks later.</td></tr>
<tr><td>Cham. law. cultivars</td><td>30 g/m^2 in 20 litres or $5^1/_2$ lb/100 yd^2 in 350 gals.</td></tr>
</table>

† Covers area of plants or pots.

Aluminium tris (ethyl phosphonate) (trade name Aliette) can also be used as a drench on low growing subjects against phytophthora.

CLEMATIS WILT. This disease has been particularly troublesome since Clematis breeding began in the mid 19th Century. It was thought until recently that the cause was due to plants being grafted but as both grafted and plants raised from cuttings are infected this theory was dispelled.

In Britain the culprit is *Ascochyta clematidina*, while in Holland another fungus *Coniothyrium clematidis-rectae* is the cause. Any part of the plant can be affected but the most common part is at ground level or just below ground level. Sometimes after shoots die new growth can come away below the infection. Leaves can carry spores so all diseased tissue should be cut out and burned.

Fungus can be controlled in the nursery by having a hygienic growing area which is cleaned out with formaldehyde, a 1 in 50 solution using 2.2 gals/1.2 yd^2 (10 litres per m^2) and leaving it for 2–3 weeks before setting plants down again.

Benomyl (Benlate), a systemic fungicide, is effective as a control using $^1/_2$ oz to 4 galls (20 gms per 25 litres) put on at 2.2 gals/1.2 yd^2 (10 litres per m^2) at regular intervals.

REPLANT DISEASE which is associated with Rosaceae plants and in the nursery trade with *Prunus* and *Sorbus* can be controlled by rotation of crops, or treating the soil with chloropicrin or formaldehyde.

3) Virus

These are even smaller than bacteria and consist of protein and nucleic acid. It is only recently that attention has been increasingly focused on virus disease in ornamental trees and shrubs. Often the effect of the virus is accepted as it gives differences in foliage or flower, for instance Arabis mosaic gives rise to variegated leaves in Abutilon and Jasminum.

Although seed is generally believed to be virus free some viruses can be transmitted this way, for instance up to 40% of Prunus necrotic ringspot which has an effect on rootstock raising and subsequent budding or grafting. Viruses are easily transmitted by vegetative propagation as well as being carried by aphis and nematodes, which makes the use of virus free stock and elimination of carriers the first requirements when tackling the problem.

Only once the viruses have been detected (as they can be latent or masked) and eliminated is the difference in growth, flower colour etc. fully realized.

Names of virus can often relate to the plant it has first been found on, such as Cherry leaf roll (CLRV) which, as well as infecting *Prunus* affects Elm, Birch and Elder.

MOSAIC is a common virus name and can, as well as infecting plants other than the one bearing its name, be specific to a particular plant.

PLUM POX (sharka). This virus attacks plum, damson, apricot, peach and other related plants. Although primarily a virus of fruit trees it will also infect ornamentals of the same type i.e. Prunus *cerasifera cv. pissardii* and Prunus *triloba*.

In England and Wales the Ministry of Agriculture must be kept informed if nurserymen propagate susceptible trees; also if Plum pox is found on the nursery.

ARABIS MOSAIC (AMV) can be found on many ornamental plants such as Buxus, Cornus, Daphne, Ligustrum, Pinus, Roses, Ruta and Salix, while poplar mosaic virus relates to the disease in Poplar. Malus species can be inflicted by some of the following viruses: Stem pitting, Chlorotic leafspot, Epinasty and decline, but seed is not a vector on Malus so the production of seedling rootstocks will give healthy stock.

Control of virus. Obviously prevention is better than cure. This would entail having hygienic conditions on the nursery to eliminate carriers of virus such as aphis which are difficult to control but can be discouraged by oil emulsions and barrier crops like Rye grown round the crop. Nematode control is more successful by sterilization, nematicides, and by leaving the ground fallow, but this will be expensive.

Obtain material which is virus free and if rootstocks are to be grown produce them from seed (except *Prunus*). Be on the lookout for signs of virus and destroy any plants infected. Avoid budding or grafting where there is a risk of spreading virus diseases. Virus can be eliminated by heat treatment but this is usually carried out by Experimental or Research Stations.

Mineral deficiencies. These can be the result of a lack of an essential food reaching the plant. The symptoms may resemble virus but can be corrected by applying the lacking nutrient either in a solution or as a powder. Chlorosis is common on Rhododendrons and may be due to various causes. If magnesium or manganese is lacking these can be corrected by either applying four sprays of 2% Epsom Salts ($Mg\ SO_4$) or Manganese sulphate 3 lbs (1.2 kg) in 100 gals of water.

Beneficial Relationships

Not all insects and fungi are harmful to the crop and the ones which aid horticulture tend to be overlooked. Ladybirds (*Adalia* and *Coccinella*) are well known for keeping aphis populations down, which in turn can lessen the spread of virus disease. Ladybirds were practising biological control before it became fashionable! Although this biological warfare has more potential within an enclosed environment there are several success stories in nursery crops. In California a wasp, (*Trioxys pallidus*) successfully combated the Walnut aphis (*Chromaphis juglandicola*). It is apparent that biological control is only practical when a large enough numbers of offenders provide food for a large enough number of the attacker.

BEES AND OTHER POLLINATORS. It is easy to be unaware of the value of pollinators and we tend to take for granted the beautiful berries on ornamental trees and shrubs. Producers of top fruit have been aware of the benefits gained from having hives in orchards. The danger of pollinators being killed by chemicals is great and the grower should be aware of the toxic chemicals he uses. (A list of chemicals can be found on page 74 of *Beneficial Insects and Mites* M.A.F.F. Bulletin No. 20, published by H.M.S.O.).

The inter-relationship between specific fungi and roots (mycorrhiza) has been known for a long time and although usually associated with forestry subjects there are few plant families which do not have this beneficial relationship. No harm is caused to the roots and in turn plant nutrients are produced.

Chapter 15

Up-to-date approach

New ideas come along all the time, some born of neccessity, others by innovation, and still more by man's ingenuity.

At the moment heat conservation is being given a great amount of attention and although not so critical for the producer of nursery stock, several ways in which heat can be easily conserved are: on mist benches the use of polystyrene sheets below soil warming cables will allow heat to stay where it is most needed, thus cutting down fuel bills by half. Turning off electricity either during the day or night has already been mentioned. If polythene sheeting is used more often to cover cuttings instead of a mist, it is useful to know that one third of the energy can be saved.

Thermal screening could be used to partition off the propagation area, should it be in a greenhouse with other crops, thus conserving heat. This would apply to the area immediately above the mist as well as at the sides.

A 'skin' can be effective if placed against glass or in polythene tunnels. Polystyrene sheets, polythene or the newer air cap are possibilities.

Although not a new idea, some tunnels are double skinned with an air flow between the skins giving good insulation. Foam, already used on overwintering vegetables and nursery stock in tunnels could be tried on seedbeds where more exotic species may need protection, or for hardier kinds against the devastation of a prolonged winter or pests. For the same reason Xiro film (perforated polythene) used frequently on vegetables since it rises as the plants form and gives protection could be used to protect stock plants. This material is also proving useful for nursery stock as not only will it cover seedbeds, although in Denmark it has been found that seedling leaves sometimes 'stick' to the film but will act as protection on batches of plants standing outside, thus cutting down the need to put up polythene tunnels.

POLYTHENE TUNNELS will be constructed more to meet the needs of the crops and the two material tunnels of woven material round the base covered by polythene on top will be put up to give hardier plants, which the public, now more discerning and knowledgeable about plants, are beginning to demand.

PLANT HEALTH A Government paper on a voluntary certification scheme for nursery stock is coming out and as this is standard practice in European countries and is compulsory if exporting plants, surely only good can come from it, especially as we could export more of our nursery stock.

PLANT PRODUCTION We are also producing more of our plant requirements in this country, thus cutting down the need to import. There is still a long way to go as we cannot yet match the expertise in selling and advertising managed so well by the Dutch Horticultural industry.

BUDDING AND GRAFTING With more plants being budded and grafted these skills have to be acquired as we are not traditionally a nation of craftsmen in nursery stock. Often courses will be run by the Agricultural Training Board to give instruction in newer techniques, as for instance in chip budding.

Work too at the Kinsealy has shown that by using paraffin wax dips on such genera as Betula, Hamamelis and Robinia will do away with the need for closed cases and the stocks can be grown on open benches.

CLONAL SELECTION Initial work has begun at Long Ashton Research Station into clonal selection in Britain with support from the H.T.A. (Horticultural Trades Association U.K.). As it is in its infancy yet, there are no definite conclusions from this work apart from the fact that it is beneficial and Long Ashton plants will be available to the trade. But as clonal selection is already standard practice abroad we will need to be more choosy in our cultivars, to give freedom from disease, correct naming and control over the release of propagation material.

MICRO-PROPAGATION. Just as other ideas and methods seemed revolutionary or 'way out' when first introduced, such as John Innes composts or Nutrient Film Technique, the same could be said for micropropagation which is also seen as a tool for research workers rather than basic production of plants. Growers in other countries (U.S.A. and Australia) have been quick to realize the potential of propagating and eliminating virus diseases by this method and carry out this technique on their nurseries. Already in Britain there is evidence of this happening and it will not be too long before an aseptic production unit is part of many nurseries and will be just as familiar as the potting shed.

NUTRIENT FILM TECHNIQUE (N.F.T.). It is perfectly feasible to produce nursery stock by growing them in gullies of flowing water and nutrients. Experimentally, several trees and shrubs have been grown by this system and a healthy mat of roots have been formed. As these are water roots there may be establishment problems once the subjects are planted outside, with more water than normal being applied initially. Also the shallower, flatter root system would probably mean that some support system would be needed at the beginning.

Possibly local authorities who use such plants for interior decor or short stay planting would find the system useful. As the potential is there (being already well established for other crops) it is now necessary to see if the plants will establish successfully in conventional soil types.

COMPUTERS. The use of computers has infiltrated more aspects of our lives and with more and more information required instantly it would seem logical to use a computer for nursery stock records.

The B.d.B. (Bund deutscher Baumschulen) in Germany have a centrally controlled data bank where instant reference can be made to the plants available on any one nursery. This leaves the nurseryman free to worry about other problems!

A Garden Centre in the Lake District has found computer time useful for stock taking and the Royal Botanic Garden, Edinburgh, knows the location of all their plants from data sheets.

Obviously computer time is expensive so co-operation in buying some time is a possibility.

CO-OPERATION. More co-operation could be a life line for nursery stock producers. No one already a member of a co-op would agree that it is plain sailing and individuals will beg to differ on many occasions, however once the advantages and the mutual benefits are realized it should be possible to present a larger united front to the customers. There are many successful co-operatives in this country and these have been already mentioned in Chapter 2.

The dissemination of knowledge is now excellent and from E.H.S. and A.R.C. and Societies with barriers broken down only good can come from the exchange of ideas and experience of research workers, nurserymen and lecturers alike.

Long may it continue!

Chapter 16

Nursery economics

The aims of nursery management are to co-ordinate and direct the overall functions of the business. This means the management team must control labour, costs and cropping; plan what to do in the future i.e. decide what will be profitable to plant and when to plant it, when to spray, harvest, etc. The manager must co-ordinate all aspects of the nursery through the growing to the selling stages and finally motivate the workforce to ensure the work gets done and to the standard required.

The aim of any business is to ensure that the outputs from the enterprise are greater than the inputs so that a profit is produced. The recipe for success in nursery production is the correct balance of land, labour and capital; if any of these become scarce then the business will inevitably suffer.

Land

Land is now an expensive commodity and represents the greatest part of a nursery's capital assets therefore it must be chosen with care, especially if the grower plans to raise field crops. Selecting the right land is important as an unsatisfactory site means additional costs in the future. Firstly, consider the physical limitations of any site; ideally the elevation should not be over 300 m and preferably below 150 m above sea level. The higher the site the colder it will be all the year around and this will result in a shorter growing season and a greater chance of the land being frozen when you want to work it.

If raising field grown plants, the soil depth is important and at least 250 mm depth is required, avoiding a stony soil if you plan to use a lot of machinery in the ground.

A grower should not pick a site that has less than 750 mm of rainfall per annum unless he plans to instal an irrigation system on the field.

Once the initial site selection has taken place, then soil analysis, local topography and access need to be studied to ensure that these meet the requirements of the grower and the crop to be produced.

Labour

For a nursery to be successful it needs a well balanced labour force. This will vary depending on the scale of the operation, degree of mechanization and availability of alternative work in slack periods. It is difficult to suggest an average labour requirement, but many field crop growers estimate one man per 0.4 ha or 1 man per 1.6 ha if the nursery is highly mechanized.

The availability of the right type of labour will vary depending on where the nursery is situated. It is often easier to obtain labour in rural areas than in areas where urban industry is offering high wages.

Fortunately, colleges, the Agricultural Training Board and National Proficiency Tests Council are all helping to raise the standards of the work force with the result that the nursery industry is now getting a more skilled labour force to carry out the many complex jobs that occur in the nursery.

Capital

Capital is the money invested for the purpose of earning money and capital costs are essential items that are required before you can grow the crop. In a nursery capital items include glasshouses (if propagating), tractors, planting machines, packing sheds, etc.

Most growers have to borrow money to obtain capital items and this needs very careful consideration as borrowing money is getting more expensive and must be carefully planned.

The source of capital can vary according to how long you require the money for. A long term loan can last for over ten years, whilst a short term loan normally lasts for not more than two years. An old saying mentions the best sources of money are patrimony, matrimony or parsimony but most of us have to go to other, outside sources.

For long term sources a grower can obtain private loans, an agricultural mortgage or go to the bank, which is still the best source. For short term loans the grower can use trade suppliers, or merchants, the bank, higher purchase or use co-operative lending, if he belongs to a co-operative.

In Scotland the Highland and Island Development Board may give loans.

There are a few fundamental principles which borrowers should bear in mind:–

(a) The loan must be for profitable purposes in the nursery; do not borrow to provide amenities.
(b) The grower must be sure that interest and capital repayments can be made out of the income whilst maintaining liquidity (i.e. ready cash in at least some part of the year).
(c) Borrow from the smallest number of sources.
(d) Repay the loan during the working life of the asset.

Prospective lenders will want to know about the past performance of the grower and his business in terms of profit, previous and present loan commitments and his or her experience at this work. They will want to know what security can be offered against the loan and what the money is to be used for.

Not only can the grower obtain a loan, but he also may be eligible for a grant from the Government. Two schemes are available for nursery stock producers and many growers take the opportunity to use the grant system.

The Horticultural Capital Grant Scheme amounts to a 25% grant for improvements to land and for buildings used for the business as well as for associated services such as ditching, drainage and irrigation. A 15% grant is given for machinery and equipment.

To qualify for a grant the nursery must cover at least 1.6 ha of land and have been in production for two years. After the approved grant proposals it must also prove to be reasonably efficient and provide a stated net annual income.

The Farm and Horticultural Development Scheme is the other grant scheme mentioned. It is designed to help growers, whose income is below average earnings in non-agricultural industry, to improve their nursery and achieve a comparable income.

A development plan must be submitted to show how the grower plans to raise the income and applicants must be qualified nurserymen with adequate experience and capable of keeping accounts. This grant provides capital expenditure on a wide range of items including buildings, drainage, equipment, land clearance, electricity etc.

Once again in Scotland the Highland and Island Development Board may give grants.

Variable Costs

Once the nurseryman has his basic requirements of land, labour and capital he must then consider each individual enterprise and study the variable costs, or the costs involved in producing that crop.

To be of use to the grower the costings must be accurate and include everything involved in that production cycle.

The example below gives the type of items one needs to consider when looking at variable costs, e.g.

ESTIMATING ANNUAL COSTS FOR BOXES OF CUTTINGS ON A MIST BENCH IN A GLASSHOUSE

Crop Output 1000 boxes a year at xp each

Variable Costs per Box = Q

1. *Material*

Box	ap
Growing Media (1 cu m fills 200 boxes)	bp
Label	cp
Hormone Powder (1 kg tin for 1000 boxes)	dp
Material costs a + b + c + d =	Yp

2. *Labour*

Collecting, preparing, inserting cuttings and placing boxes on a mist bench	Xp

3. *Running Costs*

Electricity costs of 'q' p a month per square metre	Zp

Production Cost per box = Y + X + Zp

Variable Costs per Year = YXZ × 1000

Crop Output (less marketing costs, transport, etc) = Q

Gross Margin = *Q − YXZ*

Profitable Growing

All nurserymen are in the business to make a profit, but this means careful planning and keeping records of all the costs involved. As an industry many growers also provide a wide range of plants, some of which are more profitable than others, but the variety offered means customer requirements are satisfied and it is therefore often unwise to just grow the more profitable lines.

The costing of nurserystock is often difficult compared to manufactured goods as growers have to cope with the weather, pests and diseases, plant deaths, quality variation and a fluctuating market all of which make planning more difficult.

The following table shows how the selling price is achieved, assuming the market place needs those plants, if not the profit disappears.

A Direct Material Costs + B Direct Labour Costs	= A + B Direct Costs + C Overhead Costs*	= ABC Total Costs + D Transport + E Profit	= ABCDE Total Selling Price

* Overheads would include such things as rent, repairs, bank interest, telephone, stationery, accountant fees, etc.

Cash Flow

One of the difficulties a nursery grower has is maintaining a cash flow, or the money coming in and out of the business. He has expenditure which occurs throughout the year, such as wages, running costs, etc., but his income tends to peak at certain months with some months when no income will come in at all. The net cash flow is the difference between money in and money out; it is not uncommon for a negative net cash flow to occur with the result that working capital has to be borrowed to see the grower through until he can sell his nursery stock. Consequently each year's overdraft is partly to finish off the crop to be sold later that year and partly to establish the plants to be sold next year.

Cash Flow Diagram for a Field Raised Tree Crop, Table No. 6.

Expenditure

The cash flow will vary with the different types of nursery stock as different crops need different input demands. For example, a container crop grower has a large investment at the beginning of the crop, such as pots, growing media and liner plants, all to be paid for early in the life of the crop. A field raising tree producer has a large investment at lifting time and could even sell his crop before having to incur this cost. In this situation the cash flow situation when starting a nursery is far easier with field grown stock.

Table 6 CASH FLOW IN A TREE NURSERY

INCOME

Income from Tree Sales — Income from Tree Sales

J F M A M J J A S O N D

WAGES

RUNNING EXPENSES – Electricity, Petrol, Depreciation Costs

Chems — Casual Labour — Canes Packing Materials etc. — Root-stocks etc.

Table 7 THE CASH FLOW CYCLE ON A NURSERY PRODUCING TWO YEAR WHIPS

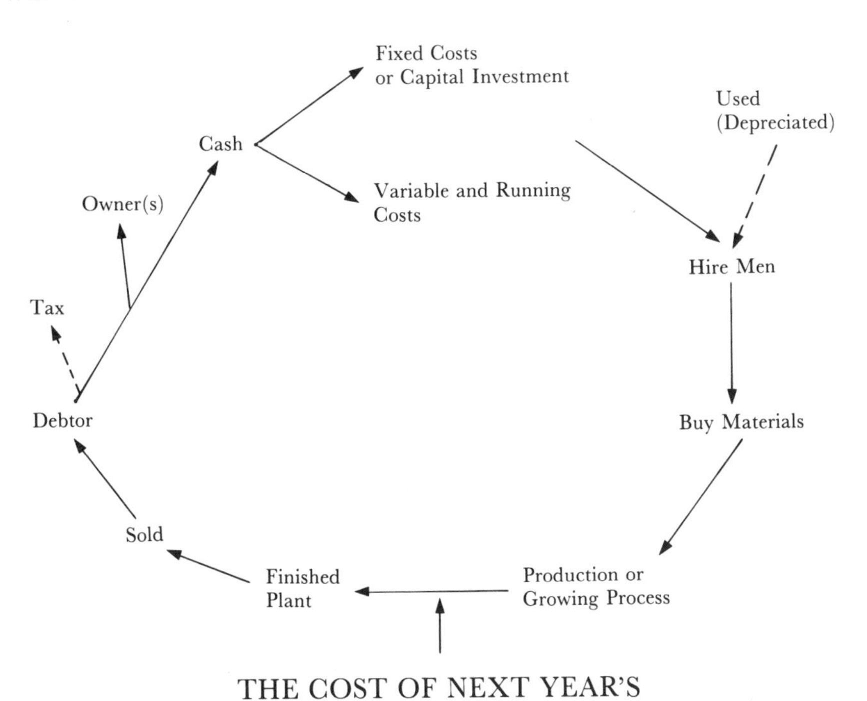

The more cash that returns from sales is 'ploughed back' into Capital Investment (new tractors, buildings and running costs) the less tax that will have to be paid on the profits of the cycle. In the production of liners this cycle will take up to 12 months, but on heavy trees it could take up to 8 years with a high cost of borrowing money for this length of time being a major factor.

Records

To be successful the nurseryman must keep records of all aspects of his business.

Financial records or accounts should include a cash analysis book which should record sales received and expenses paid. The book must have carefully chosen columns for broad expenses and record the date of receipts and payments of all money coming in and out of the business. The cash analysis book will give details which are required for the Trading account.

The Trading account summarizes the cash analysis book and is used for tax assessments. It should also include depreciation costs but not total costs of purchases of machinery or other capital items.

A Balance Sheet is used by the taxman, the bank manager and government if applying for a loan or grant. It should list the assets of the business such as crops, bank balance and money owed as well as the liabilities, such as loans and money the grower owes. Examination of a balance sheet usually indicates any ability a grower has to finance any changes in the nursery or opportunity for any additional money to be borrowed. Both the Trading Account and Balance Sheet are required to be produced once a year by law.

Apart from financial records a grower also needs to keep crop records. Crop records are notes on the past, but a grower must look at what has happened in the past before he can plan the present and the future. Records should record the minimum information that is worthwhile as it is expensive to keep records for records sake. Crop records can basically be divided into two types: crop record sheets and labour requirement sheets.

Crop record sheets should record all the variable costs including casual labour (but not full time labour) as well as marketing expenses. A labour requirement sheet should record when operations are carried out on the crop, for how long and by whom.

By using both these records the nurseryman can find out if crops are bringing in the highest returns possible and if not, why not? It should also allow him to look at individual crops and decide on which is the best combination of crops for full use of labour, maximum overall profitability and return on capital invested.

Stocktaking

The most important record which has to be carried out at least once a year by a nurseryman is a stocktaking record. He must know what he has available for sale before he can do any advertising or cataloguing.

Stocktaking is often carried out in a slack period when labour is available, but must be done well in advance of the projected sales period. It is a time consuming job, but once done information can be easily kept up to date on a card or computer system.

Stocktaking is also a skilled job requiring good plant knowledge on the part of the worker as labels invariably get lost. A suggested stock taking card is given below although the type of stocktaking varies with individual nurseries and the type of product they grow.

With all these records at his disposal a grower can make decisions on the best ways of improving his business and using his capital.

STOCKTAKING OF PLANTS

Name	Number available	Size now cm	Expected valuation	Present price	Expected	Comments

Financing

It is not always essential or desirable to purchase new equipment for the nursery and records may show that although the nursery needs a new planting machine or tree lifter, it may not be able to afford one. This may mean that the grower has to use machines without actually owning them, so that he can conserve his own capital and charge the expenses in obtaining equipment against his taxable income. There are several ways he can obtain equipment if he does not buy.

Firstly, it may be possible to employ a contractor so that the machine is used to its optimum, in this case the equipment normally comes with an operator. The disadvantages with this are that the specialist equipment the grower needs may not be available and the machine may not be available when the grower requires it.

An alternative is short term hire which many nurseries use to make maximum use of a potting machine. Normally, at first sight this looks expensive as hire is normally on a weekly basis, but on carefully studying it may look attractive if compared with buying a similar machine. Short term hire is ideal if the nurseryman can guarantee materials and labour will be available when the machine is on the premises.

Contract hire on a monthly basis may be considered and faulty machines are quickly replaced, but misuse can increase the hire charges. Many growers are now attracted to leasing equipment and buildings. Leasing arrangements vary from firm to firm and normally the user is responsible for licence, insurance, repairs and maintenance. Leasing normally continues for two to three years or more before renegotiation and normally no replacement occurs if a breakdown occurs. It may be worth pointing out that at an interest rate of 15% from the bank, the cost of repaying a £5000 loan over five years would be £1495 per annum if loan repayments and interest are allowed for. Consequently hiring and leasing are becoming more popular for although they are no cheaper than using bank money they are competitive and avoid a grower having to find the initial £5000 which could be used to better effect elsewhere in the business.

Essential Outgoings From The Business

Whether the nurseryman keeps detailed records, and is successful or not, there remains essential outgoings from the business that will be incurred. These include loan repayments, finance charges and overheads, purchases of supplies and materials and taxation.

Taxation is a contribution levied on persons, property or a business for support of the government. We all pay direct tax, which is taken at source via wages, in the form of income tax. The nurseryman is allowed tax-free expenses if they are incurred in the business and included in the financial accounts. These can include such items as stationery, postage, advertising, travel expenses and so on.

Income tax is deducted by employers who send the tax to the Inland Revenue. Indirect tax is also paid by nursery businesses in the form of Value Added Tax (VAT).

VAT is divided into two parts, an input tax and an output tax.

The input tax is paid as part of expenditure i.e. VAT paid with bills from suppliers, *where a standard rate of tax is due*. The output tax relates to the selling of the nursery goods and is the tax you charge the customer again at a standard rate. The difference between the output tax and the input tax is the tax payable to the Customs and Excise. If the input tax is greater than the output tax; i.e., due for instance to stocking up of materials, then the grower is refunded the difference.

Appendix I

Sizes for nursery stock

Inches	Metric (nearest equivalent)
6–12	150–300 mm
12–18	300–450
18–24	460–600
Ft	**M**
2–3	0.6–0.9
3–4	0.9–1.20
4–5	1.20–1.50
5–6	1.50–1.80
6–7	1.80–2.10
7–8	2.10–2.40
8–10	2.40–3.00
10–12	3.00–3.50
12–14	3.50–4.25
14–16	4.25–5.00
Standards (diameters)	
2½–3 inches	60–80 mm
3–4 inches	80–100 mm
4–5 inches	100–120 mm

* Most plant sizes appear in catalogues in cms.

Appendix II

Conversion from Metric to Imperial Units

	Imperial	Metric
Length	0.39 ins	1 cm
	3.28 ft	1m
	0.62 mile	1km
Area	0.15 ins^2	1 cm^2
	10.8 ft^2	1 m^2
	2.47 acres	1 hectare
Volume	0.22 Imperial gallon	1 litre
Volume per unit area	0.09 Imp. gallon/acre	1 litre/ha
Weight	0.03 oz	1 gramme
	2.20 lbs	1 kg
	0.94 ton	1 tonne
Weight per unit area	0.03 oz/yd^2	1 g/m^2
	0.89 lb/acre	1 kg/ha

Appendix III

Abbreviations Associated with Nursery Stock

A.T.B.	Agricultural Training Board
E.H.S.	Experimental Horticultural Station
I.P.P.S.	International Plant Propagators' Society
H.E.A.	Horticultural Education Association
H.T.A.	Horticultural Trades Association
A.R.C.	Agricultural Research Council
G.C. & G.T.J.	Gardeners Chronicle and Horticultural Trades Journal
N.F.T.	Nutrient Film Technique
B.G.L.A.	British Growers Look Ahead
I.B.A.	Indole butyric acid
N.A.A.	Napthalene acetic acid
I.G.C.A.	International Garden Centre Association
E.E.C.	Economic European Community
B.A.L.I.	British Association of Landscape Industries
I.P.R.A.	Institute of Park and Recreation Administration
I.L.A.	Institute of Landscape Architects
E.M.L.A.	East Malling Long Ashton
M.A.F.F.	Ministry of Agriculture Fisheries & Food
A.D.A.S.	Agricultural Development and Advisory Service

References

Chapter 1 – Production trends

Trees & Shrubs Hardy in the British Isles, W. J. Bean, Pub. John Murray.

Horticulture in Britain, Part 2, M.A.F.F., Pub. H.M.S.O.

A History of Gardens & Gardening, Edward Hyams, Pub. J. M. Dent & Sons Ltd.

Nursery Stock Manual, Lamb, Kelly & Bowbrick, Pub. Grower Books.

'We Grow to Sell', Pershore Refresher Course Proceedings 1978.

Garden Centres and their Customers, A. S. Horsburgh & J. B. R. Anderson, Report No. 145, Economics Division, West of Scotland Agric. College.

Containers: Production and Marketing in the '80s, Nurseryman and Garden Centre vol. 166, No. 25, June 22nd, 1978 Pub. Benn Bros. Ltd.

A Survey of Demand for Hardy Nursery Stock in Scotland (Aug. 1973), B. T. Barrett. Pub. The East of Scotland College of Agriculture.

Chapter 2 – Areas of Commercial Importance

A Guide to the German Nursery Trade, Justus Breves, Publ. (B.d.B.).

French Nursery Stock production at Orleans & Angers, A. B. Macdonald, Publ. Pershore Refresher Course Proceedings 1974.

'Gexplant' Nursery Organisation in Angers, J. de Putron, Pershore Refresher Course Proceedings 1976.

The German Nursery Trade, G. Schmidt, p. 30, Publ. Pershore Refresher Course Proceedings 1972.

Some Aspects of the Japanese Nursery Industry, Dr D. W. Robinson, p. 64, Pub. Pershore Refresher Course Proceedings 1973.

The Belgian Nursery Industry and the implications of the expansion of the E.E.C., M. L. van Broeck, p. 74, Publ. Pershore Refresher Course Proceedings 1973.

Nursery Stock production in Denmark, A. B. Thomsen, p. 328, Vol. 20, International Plant Propagators' Society Proceedings.

Propagation Practices in Scandanavia, J. B. Gaggini, p. 207, Vol. 24, I.P.P.S. Proceedings.

Focus on Eire, Nurserymen and Garden Centre, Vol. 166, No. 39, p. 26, Benn Bros. Ltd.

Chapter 3 – Stock Plants

Hardy Ornamental Stock Beds, D. Anderson, p. 136, Vol. 26, Publ. International Plant Propagators Society Proceedings.

Selection of Material when propagating Leyland Cypress, B. Halliwell, Vol. 20, p. 338, Publ. I.P.P.S. Proceedings.

Stock Plant Management, J. Stanley, p. 37, Vol. 27, Publ. I.P.P.S. Proceedings.

Improving the Quality of Hardy Nursery Stocks, J. B. Sweet, A. I. Campbell, R. A. Goodall, Publ. A.R.C. Research Review, Vol. 5, No. 1, p. 6.

Chapter 4 – Production from Seed

Seed Collection and Extraction, P. Dummer, Publ. International Plant Propagators Society Proceedings, Vol. 21, p. 228.

Hardy Woody Plants from Seed, P. D. A. McMillan Browse, Publ. Grower Books.

Forestry Commission Bulletin, No. 43, Nursery Practice, J. R. Aldhouse, Publ. H.M.S.O.

Advances in Research and Technology of Seed Edited BT. W. T. Bradnock Pub. Pudoc.

Bibliography of Seeds, L. V. Barton, Publ. Columbia.

Acta Horticulturae No. 83, p. 181, Symposium on seeds problems in Horticulture.

Problems in Raising Ornamental Stock from Seed, P. Dummer, p. 213, Vol. 19, International Plant Propagators' Society Proceedings.

Aspects of Propagation in Forestry, p. 342, Vol. 20, I.P.P.S. Proceedings.

Propagation of Acers from Seed, P. A. Hutchinson, p. 233, Vol. 21, I.P.P.S. Proceedings

Chapter 5 – Rooting Substrates and Rooting Aids

Plant Growth Substances, Prof. R. L. Wain, p. 138, Vol. 24, Publ. I.P.P.S. Proceedings.

Factors which affect the response of cuttings to rooting hormones, B. H. Howard, p. 142, Vol. 24, I.P.P.S. Proceedings.

Plant Propagation Principles and Practice, H. T. Hartmann and D. E. Kester, 3rd ed., Chapter 9, Publ. Prentice Hall.

Heating for the Propagation of Nursery Stock M.A.F.F. ADAS Leaflet 709 (1981).

Chapter 6 – Production of Plants from Cuttings

Plant Propagation, K. R. W. Hammett, Publ. David & Charles.

Plant Propagation Practices, J. S. Wells, Publ. Macmillan.

Plant Propagation Principles of Cutting Propagation, p. 1, Dr B. H. Howard, Publ. Pershore Refresher Course Proceedings 1968.

Propagation by Root Cuttings, F. H. Eley, p. 332, Vol. 20, Publ. I.P.P.S. Proceedings.

Benefit from Method Study in Cutting Propagation, G. J. E. Yates, p. 163, Vol. 25, Publ. I.P.P.S. Proceedings.

Propagation of Woody Ornamentals, Dr K. Loach, The Garden, Vol. 104, part 12, Publ. R.H.S.

Propagation of Trees and Shrubs at Kinsealy, Publ. An Foras Talúntais.

Cold Frame with Plastic in Shrub Propagation, Publ. An Foras Talúntais, p. 19 Research Report 1970.

The Complete Book of the Green House Chp. 18 Vegetative Propagation, ic. Walls Pub. Wardlock.

Chapter 7 – Propagation Areas

Practical Experiences with Polythene Structures, M. J. Hall, p. 364, Vol. 20, Publ. I.P.P.S. Proceedings.

Double Tunnel Propagation, Mrs S. Ward, p. 70, Vol. 27, Publ. I.P.P.S. Proceedings.

The Propagation Unit Layout and Equipment to aid Handling, B. E. Humphrey, p. 181, Vol. 25, Publ. I.P.P.S. Proceedings.

Rooms with a view to quality (Bedding Plants), G. C. & H. T., Vol. 186, No. 5, Aug. 3rd, 1979, Publ. Haymarket.

Chapter 8 – Budding and Grafting

The Grafters Handbook (revised 1979), R. J. Garner, Publ. Faber & Faber Ltd.

Plant Propagation Principles and Practice, 3rd ed., (Chapters 11–13), H. T. Hartmann and D. E. Kester, Publ. Prentice Hall.

Graft of Deciduous Trees and Shrubs, p. 42, An Foras Talúntais, Research Report 1977.

The Long Ashton Grafting Machine, J. S. Coles, p. 254, Vol. 21, Publ. I.P.P.S. Proceedings.

A time measurement study: Bench Grafting of Woody Plants Under Glass, J. B. Gaggini, p. 275, Vol. 21, Publ. I.P.P.S. Proceedings.

Bench grafting of ornamental trees, G. C. & H. T. J., Vol. 184, No. 8, Aug. 25th 1978, Vol. 184, No. 10, Sept 8th 1978, Vol. 184, No. 12, Sept. 22nd 1978, Publ. Haymarket.

Chip Budding, Dr B. H. Howard, p. 195, East Malling Research Station Report 1973.

Chapter 9 – Micro Propagation

Plant Propagation Principle and Practice, 3rd ed. (Chapter 16), H. T. Hartmann and D. E. Kester, Publ. Prentice Hall.

Tissue Culture for Plant Propagators, R. A. de Fossard, Publ. University of New England (Australia).

Scientific Horticulture (Journal of H.E.A.) Vol. 20, p. 57–77, Publ. Elvy & Gibbs.

Propagation of Trees by Cuttings Part 2, In Vitro, p. 74, Publ. A.R.C. Research Review, Vol. 2, No. 3.

Conifer Tissue Culture, International Plant Propagators Society, Vol. 27, p. 131.

Miscellaneous Publication No. 17, 'Multiplication of Orchid Clones by Shoot Meristem Culture, Dr M. Marston and P. Voraurai, University of Nottingham, Dept. of Horticulture.

Plant Propagation by Means of Aseptic Techniques, M. J. Stokes, p. 196, Vol. 24, Publ. I.P.P.S. Proceedings.

Chapter 10 – Growing on Substrates

Conifer Bark: Its properties and uses, Forestry Commission Record 110, J. R. Aaron, Publ. H.M.S.O.

Trial of Slow Release Nitrogen Fertilisers in Container Grown Nursery Stock, B. J. W. Morgan (A.D.A.S.) p. 83, Publ. Pershore Refresher Course Proceedings 1972.

Physical properties of peat used in Horticulture, Peat v. Plant Yearbook 1972, p. 11, Peat Research Institute, Finland.

Perlite finds increasing acceptance as growing medium, Nurseryman & Garden Centre Vol. 167, No. 8, Feb. 22nd, 1979, Publ. Benn Pub. Ltd.

Growing media 1978, Nurseryman & Garden Centre, Vol. 166, No. 4, Jan. 26th, 1978, Publ. Benn Pub. Ltd.

Horticultural Science and Soils, Vol. I. Horticultural Science. E. G. Coker Macmillan and R.H.S.

Soils and other growth media. A. W. Flegmann, Raymond A. T. Gerorge, Macmillan and R.H.S.

Macdonald Horticultural Series, Vol. II. Soil and Fertilisers. E. G. Coker. Macdonald Technical and Scientific, London.

Lime and Fertiliser Recommendations No 4. GF 24 M.A.F.F. ADAS.

Fertiliser Recommendations GF.1 M.A.F.F. ADAS (Nursery Stock Index P 61.

Chapter 11 – Growing on and Plant Management

Mechanisation and Management, Pershore Refresher Course Proceedings 1974, Pershore College.

Mechanisation of Field Production of Nursery Stock, F. M. Barrett, p. 7, Pershore Refresher Course Proceedings 1972.

Some aspects of Field Production Mechanisation, B. E. Humphrey, p. 10, Pershore Refresher Course Proceedings 1972.

Nutrition of Nursery Stock in the Open, A. R. Carter, p. 67, Pershore Refresher Course Proceedings 1972.

Nutrition and Health of Containerised Stock, Pershore Refresher Course Proceedings 1973.

Staking in Relation to Growth and Form, R. J. Garner, p. 210, Vol. 25, I.P.P.S. Proceedings.

Mechanical Handling Systems, G. C. & H. T. J., Vol. 185, No. 21, May 25th, 1979 Pub. Haymarket.

Mechanising Nursery Stock, G. C. & H. T. J. Vol. 186, No. 2, July 13th, 1979, Pub. Haymarket.

Protected cultivation at the Pershore Conference, Nurseryman and Garden Centre, Vol. 167, No. 8, Feb. 22nd, 1979, Publ. Benn Pub. Ltd.

The Great Container Debate, Nurseryman and Garden Centre, Vol. 166,

No. 30, 27th July, 1978, Vol. 166, No. 33, 24th Aug., Publ. Benn Bros. Ltd.

Emphasis on Container Production Systems, Nurseryman and Garden Centre, Vol. 166, No. 30, 27th July, 1978, Publ. Benn Bros. Ltd.

Container Plant Manual, J. Edmonds, Grower Books.

Nutrition of Field Grown Nursery Stock, Leaflet No. 642, A.D.A.S. H.M.S.O.

Chapter 12 – Irrigation Systems

Plants and Water. Studies in Biology, No. 14, J. Sutcliffe, Publ. Edward Arnold.

The Economics of Irrigation 2nd ed, C. Clark, Publ. Pergamon Press.

Irrigation, Sylvia Laverton, Publ. Oxford University Press.

Mist Propagation and Automatic Watering, H. J. Welch, Publ. Faber & Faber Ltd.

Bug Business!, G. C. & H. T. J., Vol. 185, No. 17, April 27, 1979, Publ. Haymarket.

Problems with Irrigation, G. C. & H. T. J., Vol. 186, No. 7, Feb. 23rd, 1979, Publ. Haymarket.

Irrigation Economy, G. C. & H. T. J., Vol. 184, No. 5, Aug. 4th, 1978, Publ. Haymarket.

Water needs of Nursery Stock, Nurseryman and Garden Centre, Vol. 166, No. 25, 22nd June, 1978, Publ. Benn Publ. Ltd.

Water, soil and the plant. E. J. Winter. Macmillan and R.H.S.

Chapter 13 – Weed Control

Weed Control Handbook, Vols. I & II, Edited by J. D. Fryer & R. J. Makepeace, 8th ed, Publ. Blackwell Scientific Publications Ltd.

The Identification of Weed Seedlings of Farm & Garden, R. J. Chancellor, Publ. Blackwell Scientific Publications Ltd. Oxford.

Weed Control in Nursery Stock, Short Term Leaflet No. 69, M.A.F.F.

Herbicides & Nursery Stocks, p. 20/21, An Foras Talúntais (Horticulture) 1974.

Horticultural Sprayers for Small Areas, S. T. Leaflet No. 131, M.A.F.F.

Approved Products for Farmers and Growers (Agricultural Chemicals Approval Scheme) H.M.S.O.

Disease Problems of Nursery Stock, M. E. Upstone, p. 42, Pershore Refresher Course Proceedings 1973.

Container Grown Nursery Stock (Weed Control) p. 109, Efford E.H.S. Report 1972, (1973, p. 158)

Winter Weed Control on Nursery Stock, G. C. & H. T. J., Vol. 184, No. 23, Dec. 8th, 1978, p. 22.

Herbicides for one-year liner, G. C. & H. T. J., Vol. 184, No. 7, Aug. 18th, 1978.

The effect of Weeds on field-grown Nursery Stock, J. G. Davidson, Vol. 2, No. 3, p. 76, A.R.C. Research Review.

Chapter 14 – Pests and Diseases

Garden Pests and Diseases, M. H. Dahl & T. B. Thygesen, Publ. Blandford Press.

A–Z of Garden Pests and Problems, I. G. Walls, Publ. Collins.

Nutrition and Health of Containerised Stock, Pershore College Refresher Course Proceedings 1973.

The Distribution of Viruses in Ornamental Malus and their effect on Growth, A. I. Campbell (L.A.R.S.) Int. Plant Propagators Society proceedings, Vol. 21, p. 236.

Diseases and Pests of Ornamental Plants (5th ed) Pascal P. Pirone, Publ. Wiley – Interscience.

Pathology of Trees & Shrubs, T. R. Pearce, Publ. Oxford University Press.

Virus Diseases of Trees & Shrubs, Institute of Terrestrial Ecology, J. I. Cooper, Publ. N.E.R.C.

Symptoms of Virus Diseases in Plants (3rd ed), L. Bos, Pudoc, Wageningen.

Fruit Pests and Disorders, A. Brooks, K. Harris, A. Halstead, Publ. Wisley Handbook No. 27, R.H.S.

Acta Horticulturae (I.S.H.S.) No. 86, Symposium on Fireblight.

Improvement of Woody Ornamentals, Long Ashton Research Station Annual Report, p. 42.

Fungal pathogens of Ornamentals, G. C. & H. T. J., Vol. 185, No. 6, Feb. 9, 1979, Publ. Haymarket.

Tree Pathology, W. H. Smith, Publ. Academic Press.

The Specific Replant Diseases of Cherry and Plum, G. W. F. Sewell & J. F. Wilson, p. 157, East Malling Research Station Report 1974.

Improvement of Woody Ornamentals. Long Ashton Research Station Annual Report 1975, p. 42.

Chapter 15 – Up-to-Date Approach

Commercial Applications of N.F.T., Dr A. Cooper, Publ. Grower Books.

The A.B.C. of N.F.T., Dr A. Cooper, Publ. Grower Books.

Current Developments in Nursery Practice, A. R. Carter, Publ. Pershore Refresher Course Proceedings 1976 (p. 18).

Plant Propagation using Anti-transpirants as a substitute for Mist, Dr C. E. Whitcomb, p. 45, Publ. Pershore Refresher Course Proceedings 1972.

The Way Ahead, Publ. Pershore Refresher Course Proceedings 1977.

Present Position and future prospects for the British Nursery Industry, J. Randell, p. 144, Vol. 25, Publ. I.P.P.S. proceedings.

New Frontiers in Plant Propagation, H. T. Hartmann, p. 178, Vol. 24, I.P.P.S. Proceedings.

Research into the latest techniques for propagation, The Nurseryman and Garden Centre, Vol. 167, No. 11, 22nd March 1979, Benn Pub. Ltd.

Insulation Foam Protects Conifer Liners, Nurseryman & Garden Centre, Vol. 166, No. 16, 27th April, 1978.

Clonal stock dominates discussion during nurseryman's day. Nurseryman & Garden Centre, Vol. 166, No. 30, 27th July, 1978, Benn Bros. Ltd.

Mycorrhizal associations; Hardy Woody Plants from Seed (Appendix 2, p. 53) P.D.A. McMillan Brouse, Publ. Grower Books.

Xiro Film Trial on Leylandii, Nurseryman & Garden Centre, Vol. 166, No. 43, 26th 1978, p. 22.

The Modern Nurseryman J. Stanley & Alan Toogood, Publ. Faber & Faber Ltd.

General References

An Foras Talúntais (Horticulture) Research Reports (Nursery Stock References) 1970–1977.

Container Grown Nursery Stock, M. A. Scott, Efford E.H.S. Annual Reports 1972–1977.

Green pages, V. Crichton and M. Crawfor, Publ. Granada.

A Glossary of Terms used in Propagation H. E. A., Publ. Elvey & Gibbs.

Chemicals Guide, G. C. & H. T. J., Vol. 185, No. 12, March 23rd, 1979, Publ. Haymarket.

The Nursery Stock Manual, Lamb, Kelly and Bowbrick, Publ. Grower Books.

Plant Propagation Principles and Practice (3rd ed) H. T. Hartmann and D. E. Kester, Publ. Prentice Hall.

Plant Physiology in Relation to Horticulture. J.K.A. Bleasdale Macmillan and R.H.S.

Metrication Ramsay & Taylor W & R Chambers Edinburgh & London.

Results of Experiments at the E.H.S. (Hardy Ornamental Nursery Stock 1977) M.A.F.F. A.D.A.S.

Propagation Programme

KEY

PLANT NAME

GROUPING

TREE	(1)
SHRUB	(2)
CLIMBER	(3)
CONIFER	(4)

METHOD OF PROPAGATION

SEED	S
STRATIFY	ST
SOFT WOOD CUTTINGS	C(SW)
SOFT WOOD CUTTINGS (FORCED)	(F)
SEMI-RIPE	C(SR)
HARDWOOD (DECIDOUS)	C(HWD)
HARDWOOD (EVERGREEN)	C(HWE)
ROOT	C(R)
LEAF-BUD	C(L.B.)
BUDDED	B
GRAFTED	G
LAYERED	L
MICRO-PROPAGATION	M.P.
DIVISION	D

TIME OF YEAR

1 (JANUARY) – 12 (DECEMBER)

SUBSTRATE

SAND 25% PEAT 75%	SP1
SAND 50% PEAT 50%	SP2
PEAT 100%	P
PEAT 50% PERLITE 50%	P.P.1
PERLITE 100%	PER

WOUND (DOUBLE)	W(D)

ROOTING HORMONE

(SERADIX is used in this key)

SOFT WOOD SERADIX 1	(1)
SEMI-RIPE SERADIX 2	(2)
HARDWOOD & DIFFICULT SERADIX 3	(3)

PROPAGATION AREA

SEED BED	SB
MIST BENCH	MB
PROPAGATION CASE	PC
PLASTIC COVER	P
COLD FRAME	CF

OPEN GROUND	OG
BENCH GRAFT	BG
INCUBATOR	I
EAST MALLING BIN	I.M.B.

AFTER CARE

POLYTHENE TUNNEL	P.T.
NICOFENCE TUNNEL	N.T.
PLANTED IN FRAMES	F
PLANTED IN OPEN GROUND	O
POTTED INTO CONTAINERS	C
COOL (COLD) GREENHOUSE	C.H.
GRAFTING CASE	G.C.

Plant	Group	Method	Time (1–12)	Rooting Hormone	Other Treat-ments	Substrate	Area of Propa-gation	After Care
Abelia	2	C(SW)	6–7	1		SP2	M	C – PT
		C(HW)	10–2				CFOG	O
Abies	1	S	9–1				SB	O or C
		G	4 or 9				GC	
Acer (palmatum)	2	C(SW)F	4–5	2		SP1	M or P	C – PT
		S	2–4				SB	or NT
Aesculus	1	S	10–11			–	SB	C or O
		B	7			–	PC	
		C(R)	12–2			SP2	CH	O
Alnus	1	S	10–11				SB	O
		C(SR)	7			SP1	M	C or O
Amelanchier	2	S	2–4				SB	C
		L	10–2				OG	
		D	12–2				CF	CF
Araucaria	1	S	2–4				SB or	
						CH	CH	C – CH
Azalea/								
Rhododendron								
(evergreen)	2	C(SR)	8	2		SP1	M or P	CF or
		C(HWE)	10–12			SP1	M	C – PT
(deciduous)		C(SW)F)	4–5	2		SP1	M or P	C – PT
		L	11–2				OG	
Berberis	2	C(SR)	7	2	SP1	SP1	M or CF	C or CF
(evergreen)		C(HW)	9	2 & 3		SP2		O
		S	12–4				SB	
(deciduous)		C(SR)	7	2		SP1	MCF	C or O
		C(HW)	9	3		SP2		O
		D	11–2				OG	C or O
		S	2–4				SB	CF or O
Betula	1	S	2–3				M or CH	C or O
		G	1–3				GC	C

Plant	Group	Method	Time (1–12)	Rooting Hormone	Other Treat-ments	Substrate	Area of Propa-gation	After Care
Buddleia	2	C(SW)	5–7	1		SP2	MP or P	C or O
		C(HW)	11–3				OG	O
Calluna	2	C(SR)	1–12	none or 1		SP1 SP2	MPCF	C or O
		L					OG	
Calocedrus (Libocedrus)	1 & 4	S	11		ST		CH	C – CH or PT
Camellia	2	C(LB)	2–3	2 or none		SP2 PP1	M	C – PT or CH
		C(SR)	7				P	CNT
Carpinus	1	S	10–11				SB	C or O
		G	6				GC	O
Ceanothus (E)	2	C(SR)	9–10	2		SP1	MPCF	C – PT
Cedrus	1	S	10–11				SB	C – PT
		G	8				GC	C – PT or O
Chaenomoles	2	C(SW)	6–8	2		SP2	MP	C
		C(R)	1–2			SP2	CF	C or CF
		L	11–2				OG	CF or O
Chamaecyparis (Lawsoniana)	4	C(SR)	9–2	2		SP1	MPCF	C – PT or CH or NT
		C(HWE)			W	SP1 PP1	MPCF	C – PT or CH or NT
Clematis	3	C(SW)(F)	5–6	2		SP2 PP1	MP	C – PT
		C(SR)	6–7			PP1	CF	CH
Cornus	2	C(SW)	5–6	2		SP2 PP1	MP	C or O
		SR	6–7	2		SP2 PP1	CFOG	
		HW	11–3			OG		C or O
		L	11–2				OG	
Corylus	1 & 2	L	11–3				OG	GC or O
		G	2, 8				GC	C – PT or NT
Cotoneaster	2	C(SR)	6	2	W	SP1	M	C or O
		C(HW)	10–3			SP1 PP1	MPOG	CF or O
		S	2–3			OG	SB	

Plant	Group	Method	Time (1–12)	Rooting Hormone	Other Treat-ments	Substrate	Area of Propa-gation	After Care
Cryptomeria	1	C(SR)	9–2	2		SP1	M	C – PT
		S	2–3			OG	SB	
Cupressocyparis leylandii	4	C(SR)	9–2	2		SP1	M	C – PT
		HW(E)	9–2	2	W	SP1 PP1	MPCF	C – PTNT
Cupressus	4	C(SR)	9–2	2	W	SP1	M	C – PT
		S	2			PP1	SB	C – PTNNT
Cytisus	2	C(SW)	6–7	2		SP2	MP	C – PT
		S	4			PP1	SB	C – PTCF
Daboecia	2	C(SR)	2–7	2 or none		SP1	MCF	CCF
Daphne	2	C(SW)	6–7	3		SP2 PP1	M	C
		L	11–2				OG	CF
		S	3–4				SB	
Deutzia	2	C(SW)	5–6	1		SP2PP	M	C
		C(HW)	11–3				EMB	O
	2	C(SW)	4	2		SP2PP	M	
		L					CFOG	CCF
Elaegnus	2	C(SR)	4–5	2			M	C or O
Embothrium	1 & 2	C(SR)	6–7	3		SP1PP	MCF	C or O
		C(R)	11–2				CF	C or O
		S	3–4				SB	
Erica	2	C(SR)	1–12	none or 2		SP1	MPCP	C or F
		D & L				PPP	OC	CFO
Escallonia	2	C(SR)	6–7	2		SP2	MPCF	C or F
		C(HW)	10–11				OG	O
Eucalyptus	1	S	3				SB	C – CH
							CH	or F
Euonymus	2	C(SR)	6–10	2		SP2PP	PCF	C – F
Fagus	1	S	1–2				SB	
		G	4				GC	CH PT or O

Plant	Group	Method	Time (1–12)	Rooting Hormone	Other Treat-ments	Substrate	Area of Propa-gation	After Care
Forsythia	2	C(SW)	5–6			SP2	MP	C – PT – O
		C(HW)	11–2				EMBOG	CFO
Fraxinus	1	S	9–10				SB	C or O
		G	4					OGC
Garrya	2 & 3	C(HW)(E)	2	2			MP	C
		C(SR)	10	2			CF	C
Ginkgo	1	S	2				Warm glass-house	C – PT
Griselinia	2	C(SR)	10–11				CF	O
Hamamelis	2	C(SW)	6	2 or 3		SP1P	M	C
		L	11–2				OG	O
		S	11–2				SB	O
		G	8				GC	C
Hebe	2	C(SR)	8–10	1		SP2 PP1	PCF	C or O
Hedera	3	C(SW)	4–6			SP2	MP	C – PT
		C(SR)	7–10				CF	C
Hosta	2	D	2–4				CF	CF
		S	4				SB	CF
		MP	1–3				I	C
Hydrangea	2 & 3	C(SR)	12, 5, 7	1, 2		SP2 PP1	MPCF	C – PT or F
Hypericum	2	C(SW)	5, 7–9	1		SP2 PP1	MPCF	C or O
Ilex	1 & 2	C(SR)	10–11	3	W(D)	SP1	MP	C – PTF
		C(HWE)	10–12		W(D)	SP1	CF	C – PT – F
Jasminum	3	C(SR)	7–9	2			MP	C or O
		C(HW)	10–11	2			CF	C or O
Juglans	1	S	4				SB	C or O
Juniperus	4	C(SR)	11–4	2			MPCF	C or O
Kalmia	2	S	2				M	CH
		C(SR)	8	2			M	PTF
		L	8				OG	O

Plant	Group	Method	Time (1–12)	Rooting Hormone	Other Treat-ments	Substrate	Area of Propa-gation	After Care
Kerria	3	C(SR)	6–7	1			P	C or O
		C(HW)	10–11				CF	C or O
		D	3				CF	O
Kolkwitzia	2	C(SW)	5–6	2		SP2 PP1	MP	C or O
		C(SR)	9–10	2		SP2 PP1	PCF	C or O
Laburnum	1	C(HW)	2	2		SP2	CF	C or O
		B	2					GC or O
		G	7					O
Leycesteria	2	C(SW)	5–6	3			M	C or O
		S	2				SB	OF
Ligustrum	2	C(SW)	5	2		SP1PP	MP	
		C(SW)	6–7			SP1PP		
		C(HW)	10–11				OG	O
Liquidamber	1	S	11–3				SB	C – PT
		L	11–2				OG	O
Lonicera	2 & 3	C(SR)	6–7	2		SP1	P	CO
		C(HW)	10–2				OG	O
Magnolia	1 & 2	C(SW)(F)	5–6	3	W	SP1	MP	C – PT
		L	10–2					O
		S	9				SB	
Mahonia	2	C(SR)C(LB)	2	2		SP1	MP	C
		S	8–9			SP1	SB	FO
Metasequoia								
Morus								
Normolagus								
Nyssa								
Olearia	2	C(SW)	5–6	2		SP2	M	C or O
Osmanthus	2	C(SR)	6–7	2		SP2	M	C or O
Pachysandra	2	C(SR)	7–8	2		SP1	MCF	C
		D	2–4				CF	C

Plant	Group	Method	Time (1–12)	Rooting Hormone	Other Treat-ments	Substrate	Area of Propa-gation	After Care
Paeonia	2	S	9–10				SB	GC – FC
		G	8					GC
Parthenocissus	3	C(SR)	7–9	2		SP2	MP	C – PT
		L	1–3				OG	O
Pernettya	2	C(SR)	6–7	2		SP1	M	C
		D	12–2				OG	O
Philadelphus	2	C(SW)	5–6	1		SP2	M	C
		C(HW)	10–2				OG	O
Picea	1	C(SW)	5–6	3		SP1	M	C
		G	8					GC
		S	2–4				SB	O
Pieris	2	C(SW)	5–6	2		SP1	M	C or F
Pinus	1	G	2					GC
		S	10–4				SB	C or O
Platanus	1	C(HW)	10–2				OG	C or O
		L	10–11					O
Populus	1	C(SW)	6–7			SP2	M	O
		C(HW)	10–3				OG	O
Potentilla	2	C(SR)	6–9	2		SP2	MP	C or F
Prunus	1	C(SW)	5–6	2		SP2	M	C or O
(deciduous)		C(HW)	1–2				OG	O
		L	11–2				OG	O
		B	4–7					C or O
		G	9					O
(evergreen)	2	C(SW)	3	2		SP2	M	C or O
		C(SR)	7–10				MCF & OG	C or O
Pseudotsuga	1	S	10–2				SB	O
Pyracantha	2	C(SR)	9	2		SP2	MCF	C or O
Pyrus	1	BG	4–9				OG	O
Quercus	1	S	10–3				SB	C or O

Plant	Group	Method	Time (1–12)	Rooting Hormone	Other Treat-ments	Substrate	Area of Propa-gation	After Care
Rhododendron	2	C(SR)	10–12					C or F
		C(HW)	10–12	3	W or W(D)	SP1	MPFC	C or F
		G	12–2				GC	C or F
Rhus (typhina)	2	C(R)	12–2			SP2	M	C or F
		S	3–4				SBCH	
Ribes	2	C(SW)	6	1			MP	C or O
		HW 11–12					OG	O
Robinia	1	C(R)	2			SP1	MCH	C or O
		G	1				GC	C
		S	10–2				SB	C or O
Rosa	2	C(SW)	5–6	2		SP2	MP	OC
(Hybrid Tea)		B	7				OG	O
Floribunda	2	C(SR)	9–10	3			MPOG	O
		B	7				OG	OC
Species	2	C(SW)	5–6	1		SP2	M	OC
		S(T)	10–2				SB	O
Rubus	2	C(R)	11–2			SP2	MCF	O
		D	11–3				OG	O
Ruta	2	C(SR)	7–10	1 or 2			PCF	C or F
Salix	1	C(HW)	11–2				OG	O
Sambucus	1	C(HW)	10–2				OG	O
Santolina	2	C(SR)	7–9	2			PCF	C or F
Senecio	2	C(SR)	4–10	2			PCF	C or F
Skimma	2	C(SR)	6–9	– or 2		SP1	MP	C or F
		HW	11–2				CF	F
Sorbus	1	B	7				OG	C or O
		G	2				GC	C or O
		S(T)	10–2				SB	OC
Spiraea	2	C(SW)	6–7	1		SP2	MP	C or O
		HW	10–12				OG	O

Plant	Group	Method	Time (1–12)	Rooting Hormone	Other Treat-ments	Substrate	Area of Propa-gation	After Care
Stephanandra	2	C(SW)	6–7	1		SP1	MP	C or F
		D	10–2				CF	OF
Stranvaesia	2	C(SR)	9	2	W	SP2	MP	C or O
		S(T)					SB	FO
Symphoricarpos	2	C(HW)	11–2	2			OG	C or O
		D	11–2				OG	C or O
Syringa	1 & 2	C(SW)	5–6	1 or 2		SP2	M	C or O
		G	9 or 2				GC	C or O
		L	11–2				OG	O
Tamarix	2	C(SR)	6–7	2		SP2	MP	C or O
		C(HW)	11–12				OG	C or O
Taxodium	1	C(SR)	10				CF	C or O
		S	2–3				SB	C or O
Taxus	1	C(SR)	2–3		SP	SP	MPCF	C or F or O
		G	8				GC	C or F or O
		S	2–4				SB	FO
Thuja	1 & 4	C(SR)	10–2	2		SP1	MPCF	C or O
		S					SB	FO
Tilia	1	C(SW)	6	3			M	C or O
		G	2				CF	C or O
		L					OG	O
		S					SB	C or O
Tsuga	1	S	10–2				SB	C or O
Ulex	2	C(SR)	6–7 or 9	2		SP2	MCF	C
Ulmus	1	C(SW)	7–8	2		SP2	M	C or O
		C(R)	1–2				CH	C
		G	2–3				GC	C or F
		L	12–2					O
Viburnum (Deciduous)	2	C(SW)	6	2		SP2	M	C or O
		C(HW)	10				CF	C or O

Plant	Group	Method	Time (1–12)	Rooting Hormone	Other Treat-ments	Substrate	Area of Propa-gation	After Care
		L	10–1					O
(Evergreen)	2	C(SW)	4–5	2		SP1	MP	C or O
		C(SR)	6–9				CF	CO
Vinca	2	C(SW)	7	2		SP2	MP	C
		C(SR)	9–10				CF	C
Weigelia	2	C(SW)	6–7	1 or 2		SP1	MP	C or O
		C(HW)	10–2				FOG	FO
Wistaria	3	C(SR)	6–7	2			M	C
		G	3				GC	C
		L	10–2				OG	O

Index